T. J. Day

# PLANE TRIGONOMETRY

Museum of Science and Industry, Chicago

PLANE

TRIGONOMETRY

CLIFFORD N. MILLS *Professor of Mathematics*

EDITH I. ATKIN *Associate Professor of Mathematics*

ELINOR B. FLAGG *Associate Professor of Mathematics*

Illinois State Normal University

SCOTT, FORESMAN AND COMPANY

Chicago · Atlanta · Dallas · New York

COPYRIGHT, 1947, BY SCOTT, FORESMAN AND COMPANY

Printed in the United States of America

PREFACE

THIS text is the outgrowth of the material in mimeographed form that has been used by the authors in their classrooms for several years. It has been constantly revised as the advantage of some change was considered important.

An examination of the text will reveal the following features:

1. *Easy transition to new ideas.* The subject-matter is closely connected with the mathematics the student has already had, thereby making an easy transition to the new trigonometric ideas.

2. *A challenging presentation of the subject-matter.* The values that a student has a right to expect in a new subject are clearly kept before him in a challenging manner.

3. *One new idea presented at a time.* The presentation of subject-matter follows the accepted principle of teaching one new idea at a time.

4. *Simple, direct, accurate language used.* In the presentation of new material, in the giving of directions, and in the statement of exercises, simple, direct, accurate language makes the text easy to comprehend.

5. *Plan of development of new ideas.* The authors have sought to maintain a middle ground between detailed explanations which weary the good student and concise or curtailed explanations which repel his weaker classmate.

6. *A geometrical approach.* In general, the geometrical approach is used in the development of the fundamental relationships. Many students find it simpler and more convincing.

7. *Functions of the general angle introduced at the beginning of the course.* The authors believe that the presentation of the definitions of the general angle at the beginning of the course is a strong pedagogical feature. The definitions of the functions of an acute angle of a right triangle are then merely deductions which follow from the earlier definitions.

8. *Emphasis placed on the use of the natural functions.* The complete solution of the triangle, both right and general, by natural functions is presented before logarithms are introduced.

This meets the demand for greater emphasis on the use of the natural functions.

9. *Easy approach to the use of logarithms.* The very careful and clear presentation of the meaning and the use of logarithms should help to eliminate the difficulties of the subject.

10. *New tabulation form for recording results of logarithmic solutions of triangles.* A form is offered which simplifies the recording of results when logarithms are used in solving triangles.

11. *Checking of solutions.* Special attention is given to the checking of the solutions of exercises.

12. *Interesting applications.* The exercises show a careful selection of the applications of the subject-matter in many fields.

13. *Use of tables.* Four-place tables are used in all computations in this book. However, expanded tables are incorporated for use if a greater degree of accuracy is desired.

14. *Historical notes.* The notes at the beginning of each chapter add interest by showing the human aspects of the development of the subject. In the preparation of the history notes, invaluable aid was received from David Eugene Smith's *History of Mathematics*, Volumes I and II, Sanford's *A Short History of Mathematics*, Cajori's *A History of Mathematical Notations*, Volume II, Knott's *Napier Memorial Volume*, and Archibald's *Outline of the History of Mathematics*.

15. *Review questions.* At the end of each chapter is a list of review questions covering the work of the chapter.

16. *Summary of formulas and theorems.* At the end of the book there are assembled all the formulas developed in the text, and in addition all the theorems from geometry needed in proofs.

17. *Optional material.* Teachers who know that their students have a knowledge of the meaning of *scale drawings* and how to use them may omit the exercises in Chapter I. Every student, however, should review the concepts involved. The section on vectors and vector quantities in Chapter III, and Chapter IX, on complex numbers and De Moivre's Theorem, may be omitted if a shorter course is desired.

CLIFFORD N. MILLS
EDITH I. ATKIN
ELINOR B. FLAGG

CONTENTS

CHAPTER   **PAGE**

I. INTRODUCTION: INDIRECT MEASUREMENT 1
    Historical note: How did trigonometry arise?
    1. Scale drawings
    2. Angles and their measurement
    3. Similar triangles
    Review exercises

II. RATIOS INVOLVING THE SIDES OF A RIGHT TRIANGLE
    —FUNCTIONS OF ANY ANGLE 15
    Historical note: How old is trigonometry?
    4. The tangent of an acute angle
    5. Using a tangent function to find an unknown distance
    6. The sine of an acute angle
    7. Using a sine function to find an unknown distance
    8. Trigonometric functions of any angle defined
    9. Functions of an acute angle of a right triangle
    10. Scale triangle or triangle of reference
    11. Functions of 30°, 45°, and 60°
    12. Variation of the trigonometric functions as the angle increases from 0° to 90°
    13. How to use the table of trigonometric functions
    14. How to find the sine and the tangent of an angle involving minutes
    15. How to find the cosine and the cotangent of an angle involving minutes
    16. Given a function of an angle, to find the angle
    Review exercises

III. SOLVING RIGHT TRIANGLES 39
    Historical note: The origin of the names of the trigonometric functions.
    17. Suggestions for a plan of solution
    18. Radian measure of angles
    19. Three important theorems
    20. Vectors and vector quantities
    21. Components of a vector quantity
    22. Composition of a vector quantity
    Review exercises

CHAPTER	PAGE

IV. SOLVING THE GENERAL TRIANGLE 57
   Historical note: The three basic theorems.
   23. Functions of an obtuse angle
   24. The sine theorem
   25. The cosine theorem
   26. The tangent theorem
   27. The area of a triangle
   28. Radius of inscribed circle
   29. Radius of circumscribed circle
   30. Tangent half-angle theorem
   Review exercises

V. FUNDAMENTAL TRIGONOMETRIC RELATIONS 77
   Historical note: The twofold nature of trigonometry.
   31. Reciprocal functions
   32. Sine and cosine
   33. Tangent and secant
   34. Cotangent and cosecant
   35. Sine, cosine, and tangent
   36. Verifying identities
   37. Expressing all functions in terms of one function
   38. Solving trigonometric equations
   39. Sine of the sum of two angles
   40. Cosine of the sum of two angles
   41. Tangent of the sum of two angles
   42. Sine of the difference of two angles
   43. Cosine of the difference of two angles
   44. Tangent of the difference of two angles
   45. Functions of $0°$, $90°$, and $180°$
   46. Functions of twice an angle
   47. Functions of half an angle
   48. Sum and difference of the same function of two angles
   49. Solving more difficult trigonometric equations
   50. Miscellaneous identities
   Review exercises

VI. TRIGONOMETRIC FUNCTIONS OF ANY ANGLE IN TERMS OF THE FUNCTIONS OF AN ACUTE ANGLE 99
   Historical note: Graphs of the trigonometric functions.
   51. Trigonometric functions of any angle
   52. Signs of the functions in the four quadrants
   53. Functions of $(90° \pm A)$, when A is acute
   54. Functions of $(180° \pm A)$, when A is acute

CHAPTER   **PAGE**

      55. Functions of negative angles
      56. Extended proof of the formula for the sine of the sum of two angles
      57. Graphs of the trigonometric functions
      58. The sine curve
      59. The cosine curve
      60. The tangent curve
      61. Inverse trigonometric functions
      Review exercises

VII. LOGARITHMS AND THEIR USES 113
      Historical note: A notable celebration.
      62. Computation using exponents
      63. Logarithm of a number
      64. Learning to use logarithms
      65. Logarithm of a number not specifically given in the table
      66. How to find a number corresponding to a given logarithm
      67. Exponential equations
      68. How to find logarithms of trigonometric functions
      69. How to find the angle corresponding to a given logarithm of a function
      Review exercises

VIII. SOLVING TRIANGLES BY THE USE OF LOGARITHMS . . 129
      Historical note: Logarithmic tables.
      70. Suggestions for a plan of solution
      71. Case I: Given one side and two angles
      72. Case II: Given two sides and an angle opposite one of the sides
      73. Case III: Given two sides and the included angle
      74. Case IV: Given three sides
      75. Triangulation
      Review exercises

IX. COMPLEX NUMBERS AND DE MOIVRE'S THEOREM . . 149
      Historical note: The imaginary number.
      76. Complex numbers
      77. Trigonometric form of complex numbers
      78. De Moivre's theorem
      79. Roots of complex numbers
      Review exercises

SUMMARY OF FORMULAS AND THEOREMS 159
TABLES 164
INDEX 189

How Did Trigonometry Arise?

TRIGONOMETRY was developed to meet certain needs and to satisfy human curiosity. In land surveying, in navigation, and in exploring the sky, man required a technique for solving triangles which would enable him to find heights and distances impossible to measure directly. Therefore certain functions of angles were introduced, and there followed the growth of the new science of triangle measurement now called trigonometry, from the Greek words for *triangle* and *measurement*.

Although the subject of triangle measurement had been studied for hundreds of years, and books on this subject had been published, the first book to bear the title trigonometry was written by Pitiscus, a German, and published in 1595.

So great was the interest of the ancients in astronomy that spherical trigonometry was developed side by side, or even in advance of, plane trigonometry.

Geometry enables us to construct a triangle when certain known parts are given. *Trigonometry* enables us to compute the length of the sides and the size of the angles when these same known parts are given. This is called solving the triangle.

A very important part of trigonometry, the investigation of the properties of the trigonometric functions themselves, is a later development which has significant applications in the physical sciences as well as in higher mathematics.

CHAPTER

1

Introduction: Indirect Measurement

Courtesy, Ford Motor Company

Three barley corns taken from the center of an ear placed end to end equaled one inch by the edict of Edward II (fourteenth century). A foot ranged from nine and three-fourths inches to nineteen inches. ¶ King Henry I (twelfth century) decreed that the distance from the point of his nose to the end of his thumb was the lawful yard. ¶ In the sixteenth century the lawful rod was the length of the left foot of sixteen men lined up as they left church on Sunday morning.

THE first units of length used by man were based either on parts of the human body or on some human activity. The foot, the yard, the rod, and the fathom are examples of the former. The pace, the furlong, and the day's journey are examples of the latter.

As civilization developed, it became necessary to have more clearly defined units, and gradually the government of a country began to standardize the measures to be used within the realm. In English-speaking countries the inch, the foot, the yard, and the rod became standardized units of length. These units are used directly in obtaining a length. When a yardstick or foot rule is applied directly to the sides of a room to get the length and width, we have an example of *direct* measurement.

There are many distances and heights which it is inconvenient or impossible to measure directly, such as the height of a tree, or the distance to the moon. The method then used is *indirect*

1

measurement. This means that a plan is worked out in which, after taking certain direct measurements, the required height or distance can be found by solving a problem in mathematics. About 600 B.C. Thales is said to have determined the height of a pyramid by measuring its shadow and the shadow cast at the same time by a stick whose length was known. Many other interesting and important problems are solved by indirect measurement. Examples of these are found in the aerial photography used in making maps; and in the determination of the length of tunnels, the heights of mountains on the earth and on the moon, and the distances to the sun and the stars.

Trigonometry is in part concerned with the indirect measurement of distances and the measurement of triangles. Some of the methods of indirect measurement you may have studied in arithmetic and geometry.

1. Scale drawings

In making maps, or designs, the actual dimensions generally are too large to be marked on paper. Each actual dimension is then represented by a line of shorter length. In this case, we say the actual dimensions are drawn to a given scale.

EXERCISES

1. Here is a scale drawing of a baseball diamond 90 feet square. Find the distance from home plate to second base.

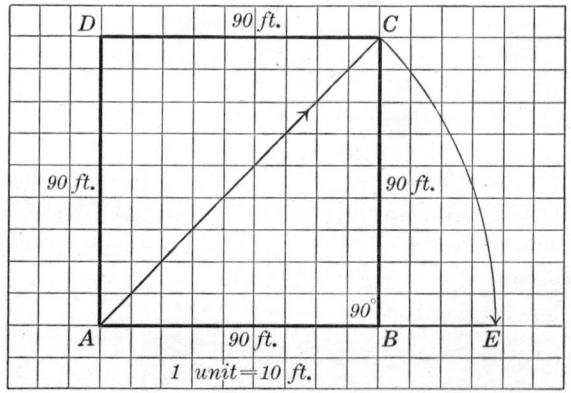

The distance may be found by measuring AC, or by drawing an arc with center at A and a radius AC cutting AB produced at E, then measuring AE. AE equals about 12.6 units or 126 feet.

INTRODUCTION: INDIRECT MEASUREMENT

2. Kingston is 120 miles north and 160 miles east of Rolla. Make a scale drawing and determine the airline distance from Kingston to Rolla. Let 1 unit = 20 miles.

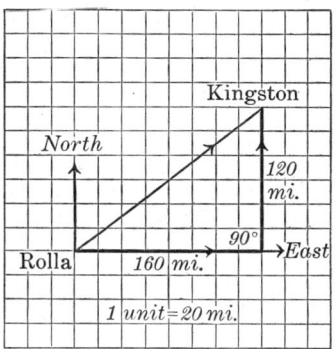

3. A man wanted to know the distance between two land corner-stones located at A and B. A small lake between the two corner-stones made direct measurement impossible. He measured due north from A to a point C, a point due east of B. Then he measured CB. AC was 200 yards, and CB was 300 yards. Make a scale drawing and find the distance between the corner-stones. Let 1 unit = 50 yards.

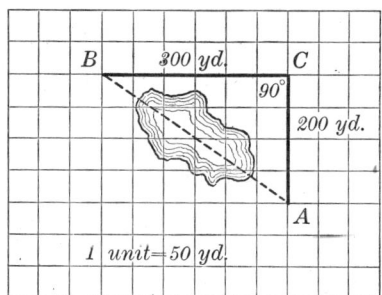

2. Angles and their measurement

An angle is formed when two lines proceed from the same point. OA and OB proceeding from the point O form an angle AOB. The size of the angle depends upon the amount of turning necessary to pass from OA to OB.

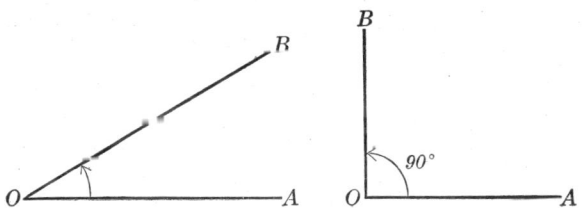

When the line *OB* makes one-fourth of a revolution, a right angle is formed. A right angle may be used as a measure of an angle, but because of its size it is not a convenient unit. A much better unit is the *degree*, which is one-ninetieth of a right angle. You are familiar with the following degree or sexagesimal table.

60 seconds = 1 minute.
60 minutes = 1 degree.
90 degrees = 1 right angle.

43 degrees, 24 minutes, 18 seconds is represented in the following manner: 43° 24′ 18″.

Mechanical measure of an angle. An instrument called a protractor is used to measure the size of an angle. A picture of a protractor is shown in the figure.

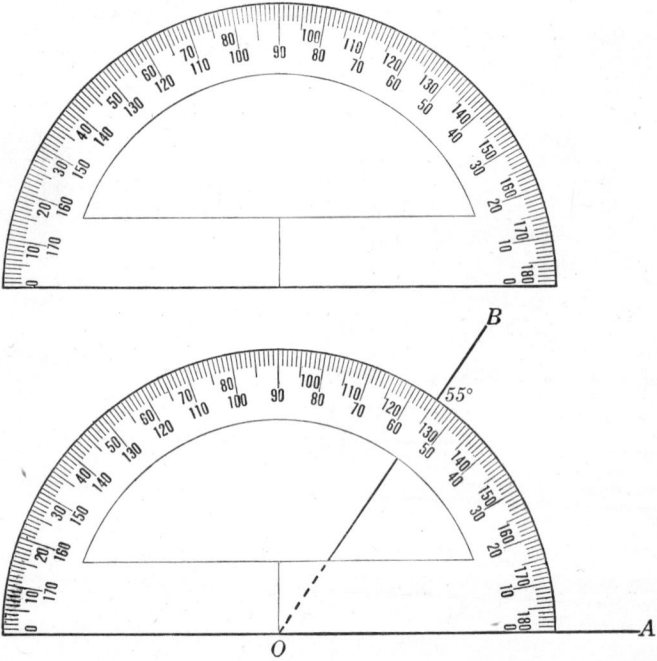

To measure an angle with a protractor, place the center of the diameter of the protractor at the vertex of the angle with the diameter along one side of the angle. Take the reading where the other side of the angle intersects the arc upon which are marked the degrees. In the figure the line *OB* cuts the arc on the protractor at a mark indicating 55°.

INTRODUCTION: INDIRECT MEASUREMENT

EXERCISES

1. With a protractor draw an angle of: 30°; 60°; 20°; 55°; 90°.
2. Measure the angles in the figures.

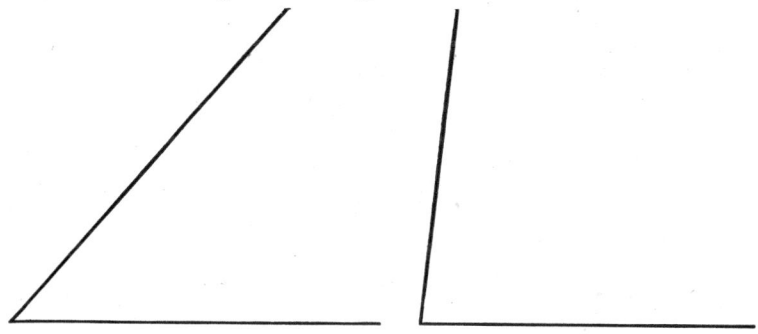

3. Two points, A and B, 600 feet apart, are on the same side of a river, B being due east of A. From a boy standing at A, the direction

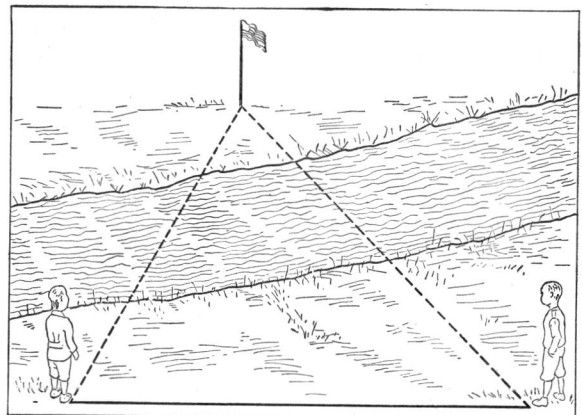

of a flagpole on the opposite side of the river was 30° east of north. From a boy standing at B, the direction of the flagpole was 45° west of north. Make a scale drawing as shown here, and find the distance from each boy to the flagpole.

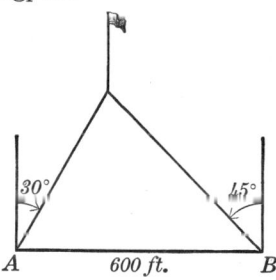

4. Two airplanes started from the same airport. One plane flew at an average speed of 100 miles an hour in a direction of 30° west of south. The other plane flew at an average speed of 60 miles an hour in a direction of 45° east of north. How far apart were the planes at the end of two hours?

Vertical line. The line determined by the direction of a plumb line at any point is called the vertical line through that point.

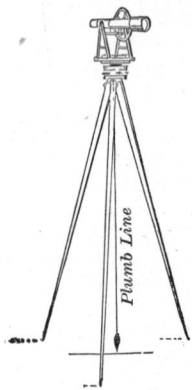

Horizontal line. A line which is perpendicular to the vertical line at any point is called the horizontal line through that point.

Angle of elevation. When you are looking up at the top of a hill, the "line of sight" makes an angle with the horizontal line passing through the eye. This angle, ∠ AOB in the figure, is called the angle of elevation.

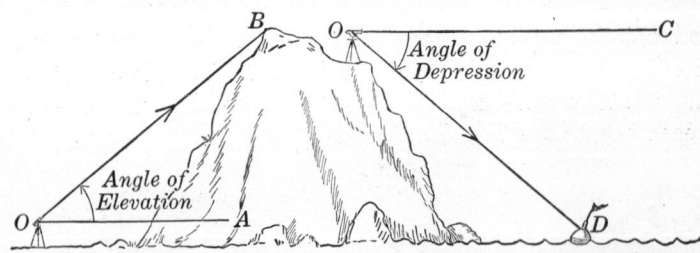

Angle of depression. When you are looking down at a point on a lower level, the "line of sight" makes an angle with the horizontal line passing through the eye. This angle, ∠ COD in the figure, is called the angle of depression.

INTRODUCTION: INDIRECT MEASUREMENT

EXERCISES

1. A boy stood in front of a tower and observed the angle of elevation of the top to be 80°. He then walked 100 feet farther from the base of the tower and observed that the angle of elevation at that point was 48°. Make a scale drawing and determine the height of the tower.

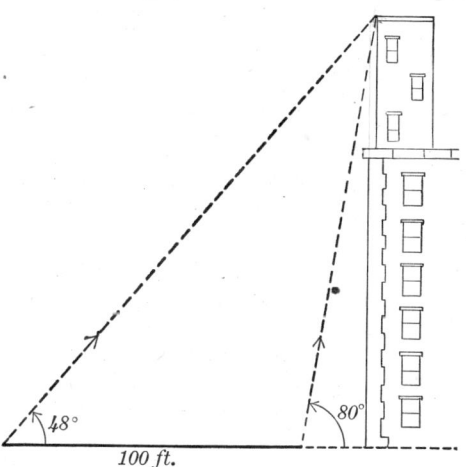

2. An observation tower is known to be 300 feet high. From the top of the tower the angle of depression of a stone-marker on the ground is 30°. Make a scale drawing and find the distance of the marker from the base of the tower.

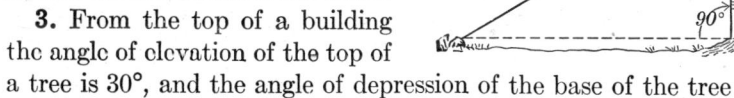

3. From the top of a building the angle of elevation of the top of a tree is 30°, and the angle of depression of the base of the tree is 45°. The tree is 60 feet from the building. Determine the height of the tree.

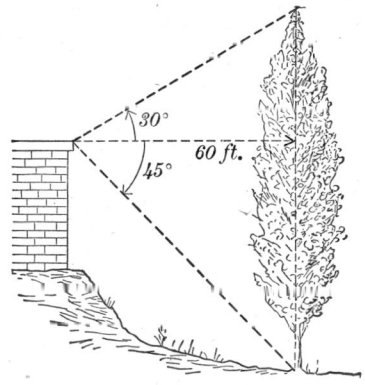

4. A tunnel to a coal mine makes an angle of 20° with the horizontal. A vertical air-shaft to the tunnel is to be dug beginning 400 feet from the entrance to the tunnel. Find the depth of the shaft and the distance from the entrance to the point where the shaft meets the tunnel. (Assume that the surface of the ground is level.)

Bearing of a line in a horizontal plane. The bearing of a line in a horizontal plane is the horizontal angle which the line makes with the north and south line through the point of observation. In the figure the bearing of the line AB is North 30° East, written N. 30° E. The bearing of the line AC is S. 40° W.

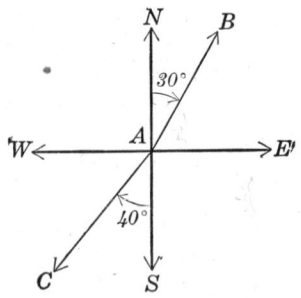

EXERCISES

1. An airplane was flying due west at an average speed of 90 miles an hour. At noon the pilot observed a signal tower to be N. 10° E. At 12:20 the bearing of the tower was N. 20° E. Determine when the airplane was nearest the tower and its distance from the tower.

2. A steamer is headed due east, having a uniform speed. At 9 P.M. a lighthouse is observed to be S. 40° E. At 11 P.M. the bearing of the lighthouse is S. 40° W. The nearest distance of the steamer to the lighthouse is 8 miles. Find the speed of the steamer.

3. A railroad track bears N. 75° E. Another track which crosses the first track bears N. 10° E. At 12:35 P.M. a train traveling in a direction N. 75° E. passes the crossing at a speed of 45 miles an hour. Two minutes later a train traveling in a direction N. 10° E. passes the crossing at a speed of 60 miles an hour. How far apart will the trains be 15 minutes after the first train passes the crossing?

4. At a point 8 feet above the surface of a pond the angle of elevation of the top of a tree at the edge of the pond is 45°. The angle of depression of the lowest part of the image is 60°, refraction neglected. The length of the image appears to be the same as the height of the

INTRODUCTION: INDIRECT MEASUREMENT

tree. What is the height of the tree? *Hint:* In the scale drawing make $AB = AC$.

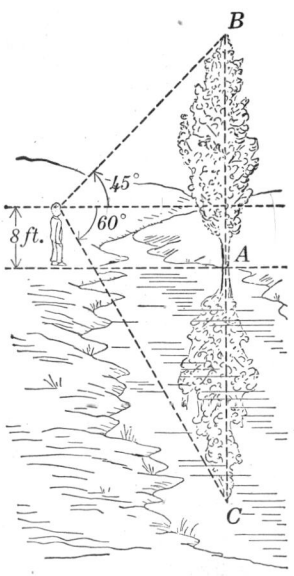

5. *Special method to determine an inaccessible distance.* To determine the horizontal distance between two inaccessible points, D and C, we may proceed as follows. First measure a base line AB; then measure the angles ABC, ABD, BAC, and BAD. Make a scale drawing using the data and then measure DC.

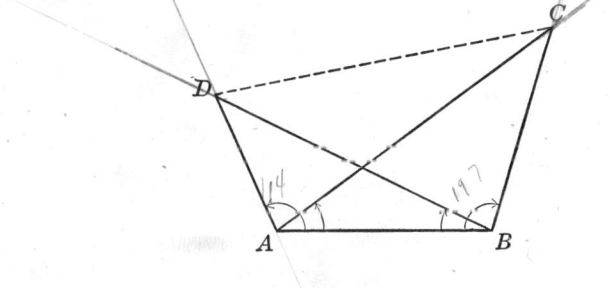

6. Two flagpoles are on opposite sides of a pond. A base line AB is marked off 600 feet in length. From the point A the bearing of the flagpole at D is N. 10° W., and the bearing of the flagpole at C is N. 55° E. From the point B the bearing of the flagpole at D is N. 60° W., and the bearing of the flagpole at C is N. 16° E. Find the horizontal distance between the flagpoles.

3. Similar triangles

In the figure, the triangle ABC is similar to the triangle DEF.

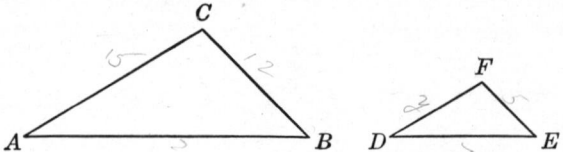

You have learned the following facts about similar triangles:
(1) The corresponding angles are equal; that is,
$$\angle A = \angle D, \quad \angle B = \angle E, \quad \angle C = \angle F.$$
(2) The corresponding sides are opposite corresponding angles.
(3) The ratios of the pairs of corresponding sides are equal, thus,
$$\frac{AB}{DE} = \frac{AC}{DF} = \frac{CB}{FE}.$$
By a principle of proportion,
$$\frac{AB}{AC} = \frac{DE}{DF}, \quad \frac{AB}{CB} = \frac{DE}{FE}, \quad \frac{AC}{CB} = \frac{DF}{FE}.$$

Example

If $AB = 16$ inches, $DF = 6$ inches, and $AC = 12$ inches, find DE.
Let x represent the number of inches in the length of DE.
The length of DE is 8 inches.

$$\frac{x}{16} = \frac{6}{12}.$$
$$12x = 96.$$
$$x = 8.$$

EXERCISES

1. In two similar triangles the sides of the larger are 12 inches, 15 inches, and 20 inches, and the shortest side of the smaller triangle is 5 inches. Find the other sides of the smaller triangle.

2. A tree casts a shadow 50 feet long when a vertical rod 6 feet high casts a shadow 5 feet long. Find the height of the tree.

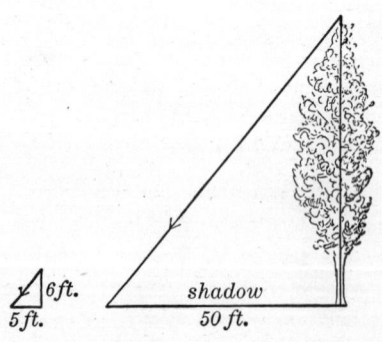

INTRODUCTION: INDIRECT MEASUREMENT

Let x represent the number of feet in the height of the tree. Then
$$\frac{x}{50} = \frac{6}{5}.$$
Solving this equation, $x = 60$. The tree is 60 feet high.

3. The shadow of a building was 96 feet long. At the same time a post 12 feet high made a shadow 8 feet long. Find the height of the building.

4. When a church tower casts a shadow $42\frac{1}{2}$ feet long, a rod 8 feet high casts a shadow $2\frac{1}{2}$ feet long. What is the height of the tower?

5. A boy wanted to know the height of a flagpole. He measured its shadow and found it to be 217 feet long. He observed that a yardstick at the same time made a shadow 7 feet long. Find the height of the flagpole.

Further use of similar triangles. The distance between two points on opposite sides of a river may be obtained in the following manner. Let A and B represent the given points. Along the

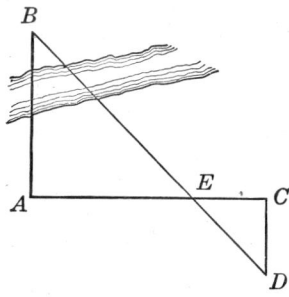

shore measure a line AC perpendicular to AB; then measure a line CD perpendicular to AC. Mark the point E on AC which is in line with DB; measure AE and EC. The triangles DEC and AEB are similar. Why?

$$\text{Then } \frac{AB}{AE} = \frac{DC}{EC}. \quad \text{Hence } AB = \frac{AE \times DC}{EC}.$$

EXERCISES

1. If $AE = 120$ feet, $DC = 60$ feet, $EC = 20$ feet, find AB.

2. Two camps were on opposite sides of a lake. Two boys wanted to know the distance between the flagpoles of the camps, located at A and B. They drove a stake at C to which they could measure from both A and B. They measured AC (100 yd.) and extended it 20 yards to A'. BC (200 yd.) was measured and then extended 40 yards to B'.

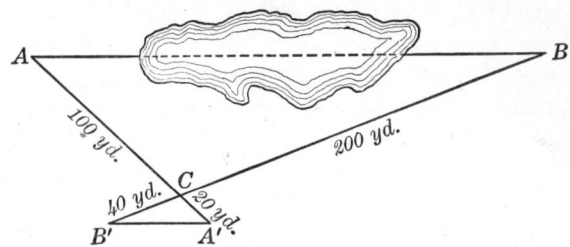

The triangles ABC and $A'B'C$ are similar. Why? What line should be measured to determine the distance AB?

3. AB is how many times $A'B'$? If $A'B'$ is 50 yards, AB is how many yards?

4. A and B are two observing stations on opposite sides of a lake. A point C is selected; AC is found to be 600 yards. CA' is measured off 300 yards; $B'A'$ is found to be 400 yards. What is the distance AB?

REVIEW QUESTIONS ON CHAPTER I

1. Explain what is meant by direct measurement. Illustrate.

2. Explain what is meant by indirect measurement. Illustrate.

3. How is an angle formed? Upon what does its size depend?

4. Define vertical line; horizontal line.

5. Define angle of elevation; angle of depression; bearing of a line. Draw figures to illustrate each.

6. What is meant by a scale drawing?

7. The top of a building is known to be 120 feet above the level of the water in a river. From a point on the top of the building in a direction at a right angle with the river, the angle of depression of a stake at the nearer edge of the river is 45°. The angle of depression of a stake at the opposite edge of the river is 15°. Make a scale drawing, and from it determine the width of the river.

8. Two camps are located on the west side of a lake. Their flagpoles, $\frac{3}{4}$ of a mile apart, are at points R and S. The point R is due south of the point S. From a point A on the opposite side of the lake the flagpole at R has a bearing of S. 30° W., and the flagpole at S has a bearing of N. 70° W. The observer moves $\frac{1}{2}$ mile due north of A to a point B. Make a scale drawing and from it find the bearing of R and S from the point B.

9. A stake at M is located between two stakes A and B, 20 feet from A and 50 feet from B. The line CD intersects the line AB at M. The distance between M and C is 30 feet; between M and D is 75 feet; between A and C is 24 feet. Use the method of similar triangles to determine the distance from D to B.

INTRODUCTION: INDIRECT MEASUREMENT 13

10. A flagpole is situated on top of a tower. At a point which is 300 feet from the base of the tower, the angle of elevation of the top of the tower is 15°, and the angle of elevation of the top of the flagpole is 20°. Find the height of the tower and the length of the flagpole. Make a scale drawing.

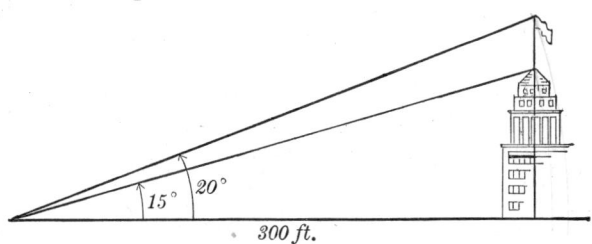

11. From an observation balloon the angles of depression of two successive milestones were 45° and 60°. The milestones were on a level road and on opposite sides of the balloon. How high was the balloon? Make a scale drawing.

12. A wooden right triangular frame may be used to determine the height of a tree. Keeping the base of the triangle level, the observer moves to a position where the line of sight along the hypotenuse points to the top of the tree. Then the observer measures the horizontal distance from his eye to the tree. Knowing the dimensions of the triangular frame, by similar triangles you can determine the height of the tree. In the figure if $AB = 16$ inches and $BC = 12$ inches, and the distance $AD = 60$ feet, find the height of the tree. The observer's eye is 5 feet above the ground.

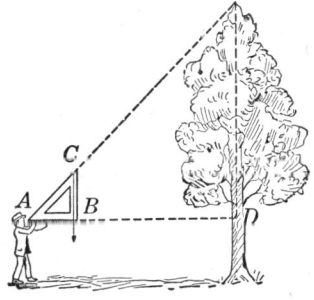

How Old Is Trigonometry?

IT IS impossible to tell definitely how old trigonometry is. Various ages are suggested by the historian, depending on what is meant by the beginning of the subject.

In the Ahmes Papyrus, an Egyptian mathematical manuscript of about 1650 B.C., is found the term *seked*. Most Egyptologists interpret this word to refer to the quotient found by dividing the distance from the center of the base of a pyramid to a side, by the height. This is equivalent to our cotangent of the angle which the lateral face makes with the base. If we accept this birthdate, trigonometry is nearly thirty-six hundred years old.

Most historians ascribe the beginning of a scientific study of trigonometry to the second century B.C. when Hipparchus, the famous Greek astronomer, constructed a table of chords, the forerunner of our tables of sines. This viewpoint makes trigonometry about twenty-one hundred years old.

If we consider the date of the appearance of the first separate treatise on triangle measurement as marking the birth of trigonometry, then we turn to about the year 1250, and the book written by the Persian astronomer, Nasir-Eddin. Or if European sources only are considered, we refer to the year 1533, when *De Triangulis*, a work on plane and spherical trigonometry by the German mathematician Regiomontanus, was published.

If, however, in considering the age of trigonometry, we include in the subject the use of modern algebraic symbolism, decimals, logarithms, a system of rectangular coördinates, and De Moivre's theorem—all found in modern texts—then trigonometry is only about two hundred years old.

CHAPTER

II

Ratios Involving the Sides of a Right Triangle—Functions of Any Angle

YOU have now studied two methods of determining unknown distances: the method of scale drawing and the method of similar triangles. These methods have certain disadvantages. The solution of some problems may become quite tedious. Others require too many measurements which may be very inaccurate. The method now to be given involves less effort and gives a greater degree of accuracy. In many problems involving the finding of the angles and sides of triangles we need to use certain ratios which have the general name, *trigonometric functions*.

4. The tangent of an acute angle

We will associate every angle with a right triangle. In the figure the acute angle A is associated with the right triangle ABC.

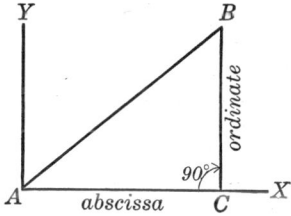

This triangle (right angle at C) has been placed on the coördinate

15

axes so that the vertex A falls at the origin and the line AC falls along the X-axis, positive direction. Since C is a right angle, CB is perpendicular to the X-axis. In this triangle the side CB is the *ordinate* of the point B, and the side AC is the *abscissa* of the point B. The ratio $\dfrac{CB}{AC}$ is called the *tangent of angle* A (written $\tan A$).

$$\tan A = \frac{\text{ordinate of point } B}{\text{abscissa of point } B}.$$

In the following figure we have four similar right triangles. You have learned that the corresponding sides of similar triangles have the same ratio.

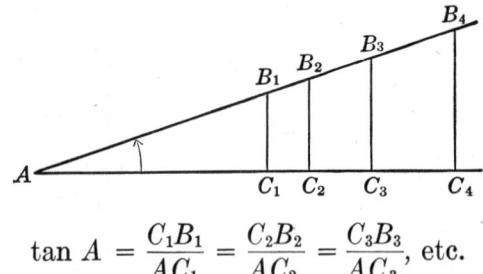

Then $\qquad \tan A = \dfrac{C_1 B_1}{AC_1} = \dfrac{C_2 B_2}{AC_2} = \dfrac{C_3 B_3}{AC_3}$, etc.

The equality of these ratios shows that the tangent of an angle does not depend upon the sides of the right triangle, but depends only upon the size of the angle. For this reason, the tangent ratio is called the tangent *function* of the angle A.

EXAMPLE

Find the tangent of 42°.

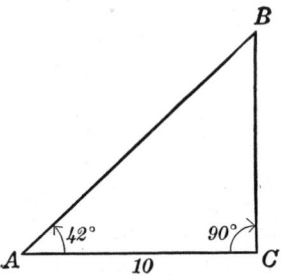

Draw a right triangle with a base 10 centimeters long, having angle $A = 42°$. Measure the length of CB. You will find that the ratio $\dfrac{CB}{AC} =$ about .9. Then $\tan 42° = .9$.

RATIOS INVOLVING THE SIDES OF A RIGHT TRIANGLE 17

EXERCISES

Check the tangent values for the given angles. Construct each right triangle with a base of 10 centimeters.

Angle	10°	20°	30°	35°	45°	50°	60°	65°	70°	75°	80°
Tangent	.18	.36	.58	.70	1	1.19	1.73	2.14	2.75	3.73	5.67

5. Using a tangent function to find an unknown distance

EXAMPLE

At a certain time of day the rays of the sun made an angle of 42° with the horizontal. The length of the shadow of a chimney was 240 feet. Find the height of the chimney.

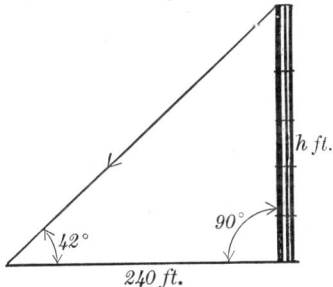

Let h represent the number of feet in the height. Then

$$\frac{h}{240} = \tan 42°.$$
$$h = 240 \times .9 = 216.$$

The height of the chimney is 216 feet.

EXERCISES

In these exercises use the values of tangents given in the table above.

1. When the sun's rays make an angle of 60° with the horizontal, the shadow of a flagpole is 62 feet long. Find the height of the flagpole.

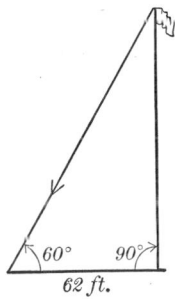

2. At the point A the angle of elevation of the top of a tree is $50°$. From A to the base of the tree is 100 feet. Find the height of the tree.

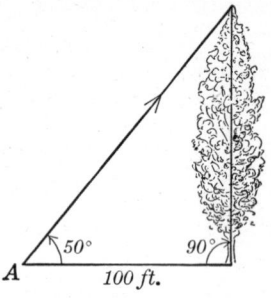

3. An observation tower on a building is 600 feet above the level ground. From this tower the angle of depression of a boat is $10°$. How far away from the base of the building is the boat?

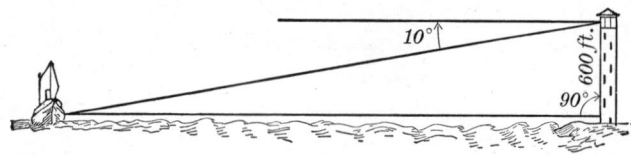

4. In this figure, B and C represent two houses on opposite sides of a river. A distance of 200 feet is measured off at a right angle to CB. Angle A is $60°$. Find the distance between the two houses.

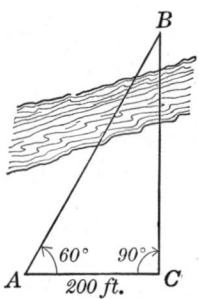

5. A flagpole 100 feet high makes a shadow 275 feet long. Find the angle of elevation of the sun.

6. When a house 65 feet high makes a shadow 65 feet long, what is the angle of elevation of the sun?

7. A boy stood in front of a church and observed that the angle of elevation of the top of the spire was $60°$. He then walked 200 feet farther away from the church, and the angle of elevation of the top of the spire was $30°$. Find the height of the top of the spire.

RATIOS INVOLVING THE SIDES OF A RIGHT TRIANGLE

From the two right triangles ADC and BDC we get
$$y = x \tan 60°.$$
$$y = (x + 200) \tan 30°.$$

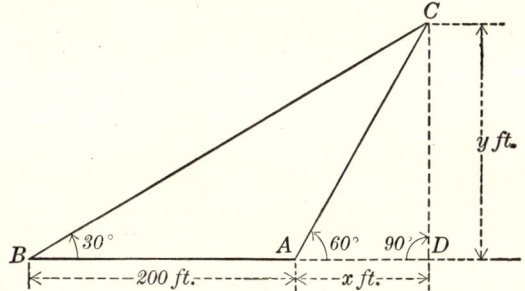

Solve the two equations for x and y.
$$x \tan 60° = (x + 200) \tan 30°.$$
$$x \tan 60° = x \tan 30° + 200 \tan 30°.$$
$$x (\tan 60° - \tan 30°) = 200 \tan 30°.$$
$$x = \frac{200 \tan 30°}{\tan 60° - \tan 30°} = \frac{200 \times .58}{1.73 - .58} = 100.87.$$
$$y = 100.87 \times 1.73 = 174.51.$$

The height of the spire is 174.51 feet.

8. Find the values of x and y for problem 7 when the angles of elevation are 45° and 30° and the distance AB is 300 feet.

9. When the angle of elevation of the sun changed from 30° to 10°, the length of a shadow of a tree increased 120 feet. Find the height of the tree.

10. A bridge across a valley is 800 feet long. At one end of the bridge the side of the valley makes an angle of 30° with the horizontal. At the other end of the bridge the angle is 65°. Find the depth of the valley.

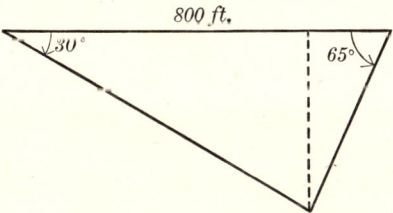

6. The sine of an acute angle

Every angle will be associated with a right triangle. In the figure, angle A is associated with the right triangle ABC. This

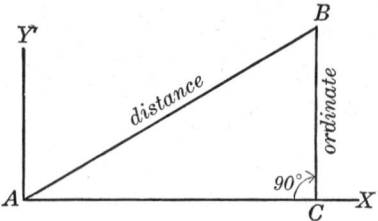

triangle has been placed with the vertex A at the origin of coordinate axes, and AC coinciding with the X-axis. The side CB is the ordinate of the point B; the side AB, the hypotenuse, is called the *distance* of B from A. The ratio $\dfrac{CB}{AB}$ is called the *sine of angle A* (written *sin A*).

$$\sin A = \frac{\text{ordinate of } B}{\text{distance}}.$$

In the similar right triangles shown here the angle A is common.

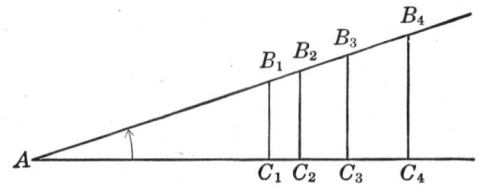

$$\sin A = \frac{C_1 B_1}{AB_1} = \frac{C_2 B_2}{AB_2} = \frac{C_3 B_3}{AB_3}, \text{ etc.}$$

The equality of these ratios shows that the sine of an angle does not depend upon the lengths of the sides of the right triangle, but depends only upon the size of the angle. For this reason the sine ratio is called the sine *function* of the angle A.

Example

Find the sine of 37°.

Draw a right triangle ABC, having a hypotenuse AB of 10 centimeters and acute angle $A = 37°$. Measure CB. You will find that the ratio $\dfrac{CB}{AB}$ is about $\tfrac{6}{10} = .6$. Then $\sin 37° = .6$ approximately.

EXERCISES

Check the following approximate sine values for the given angles. Construct each right triangle with a hypotenuse of 10 centimeters.

RATIOS INVOLVING THE SIDES OF A RIGHT TRIANGLE

Angle	10°	20°	30°	40°	60°	75°	80°
Sine	.17	.34	.50	.64	.87	.97	.98

7. Using a sine function to find an unknown distance

EXAMPLES

1. Two trees located at B and C are separated by a lake. It is required to find the distance between the trees. At a point C a line CA

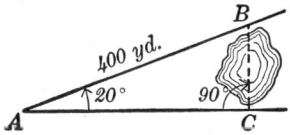

is sighted at a right angle to CB. AB is then measured and found to be 400 yards. Angle BAC is measured and found to be 20°. Then

$$\frac{CB}{400} = \sin 20°.$$
$$CB = 400 \times .34 = 136.$$

The distance between the trees is 136 yards.

2. A boy wishes to determine the height of his kite when 200 yards of string are out.

Assume that the kite string is a straight line. The boy finds that the angle of elevation is 60°. Then

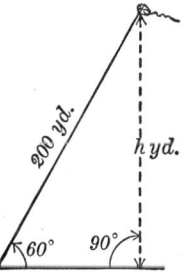

$$\frac{h}{200} = \sin 60°.$$
$$h = 200 \times .87 = 174.$$

The height of the kite is 174 yards.

EXERCISES

1. A telephone pole stands on level ground, and a guy wire known to be 50 feet long extends from the top of the pole to the bottom of a stake on the ground, making an angle of 40° with the horizontal. How high is the pole?

2. A ladder is 32 feet long. When in use it can be set with safety at as large an angle as 75° with the horizontal. How high up on the side of a wall will it reach when it makes an angle of 75° with the horizontal?

3. A surveyor wishes to find the width PQ across a river from north to south. At the point A, which is directly west of Q, he finds the angle QAP to be 40°. He measures the distance AP and finds it to be 725 feet. Find the distance PQ.

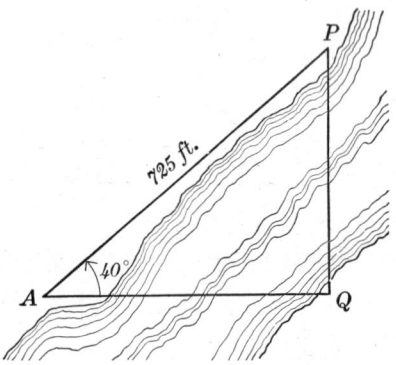

4. In a circle of radius 100 feet a chord subtends an angle of 80° at the center. Find the length of the chord.

5. A pendulum 39.1 inches long swings through an angle of 20°. What is the horizontal distance between the two extreme positions of the end of the pendulum?

8. Trigonometric functions of any angle defined

On page 16 is defined the *tangent of an acute angle*, and on page 20 is defined the *sine of an acute angle*. Frequently we have need for other ratios, or functions of an angle of any size. We shall proceed now to a discussion leading to the definitions of the six fundamental ratios. The names of these ratios, or functions, are *sine, cosine, tangent, cotangent, secant,* and *cosecant*.

On page 3 you have learned that an angle is formed when two lines proceed from the same point. It is convenient sometimes to think of an angle being formed when a line rotates about a

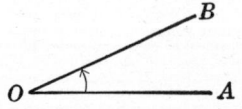

RATIOS INVOLVING THE SIDES OF A RIGHT TRIANGLE

fixed point from one position to another position. Thus the angle AOB may be formed by rotating the line OA in a counter-clockwise direction about the fixed point O from the position OA to the new position OB. OA is called the *initial line*, and OB is called the *terminal line*.

In elementary algebra you have learned what is meant by a system of rectangular coördinate axes. Choose two lines, OX and OY, as a system of axes. Let the initial line, or base line, of the angle A be OX. The terminal line of the angle can be in any quadrant. Select a point P on the terminal line of the angle. The coördinates of the point P are (x,y).

When an angle is placed with its vertex at the origin of axes, and its initial line on the X-axis in the positive direction, it is customary to say that the angle is in the quadrant where its terminal side lies. See figures below. Thus when angle A is acute, the angle is said to be in the first quadrant. When the angle is obtuse, it is said to be in the second quadrant. An angle of 200° lies in the third quadrant.

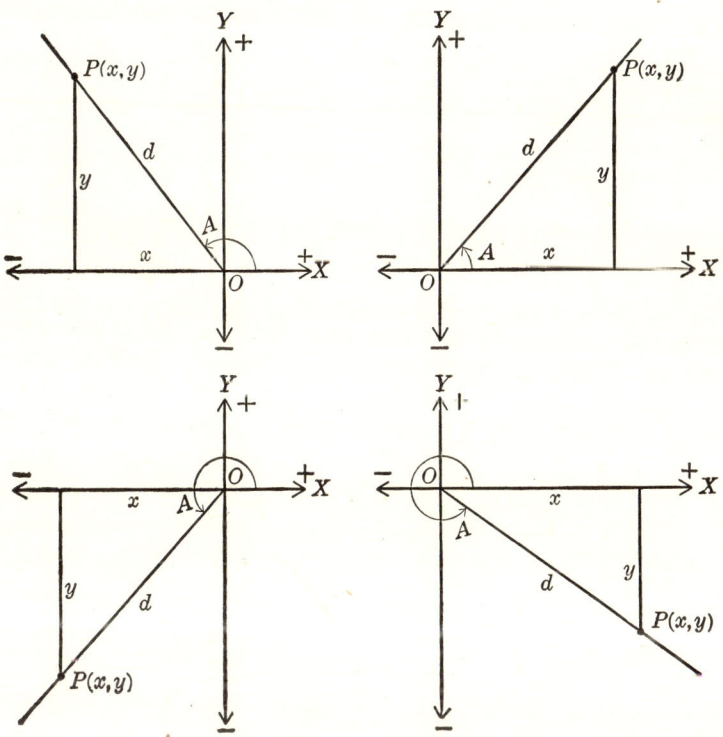

The values of x and y are positive or negative according to the quadrant in which the point P is situated. The line segment OP is called the *distance*, and the number of units in OP is represented by d. The value of d is chosen positive.

You have learned in algebra that when a point P whose coördinates are (x,y) is located with reference to a set of perpendicular axes, the x-distance is called the *abscissa* and the y-distance is called the *ordinate*. In the figure on page 23 where A is an acute angle, sin A may be written $\frac{y}{d}$ or $\frac{\text{ordinate}}{\text{distance}}$; tan A may be written $\frac{y}{x}$ or $\frac{\text{ordinate}}{\text{abscissa}}$.

The six fundamental ratios for the angle A when the terminal side of the angle lies in any quadrant are defined as follows:

$$\text{Sine of angle } A = \frac{\text{ordinate of } P}{\text{distance } OP} = \frac{y}{d}.$$

$$\text{Cosine of angle } A = \frac{\text{abscissa of } P}{\text{distance } OP} = \frac{x}{d}.$$

$$\text{Tangent of angle } A = \frac{\text{ordinate of } P}{\text{abscissa of } P} = \frac{y}{x}.$$

$$\text{Cotangent of angle } A = \frac{\text{abscissa of } P}{\text{ordinate of } P} = \frac{x}{y}.$$

$$\text{Secant of angle } A = \frac{\text{distance } OP}{\text{abscissa of } P} = \frac{d}{x}.$$

$$\text{Cosecant of angle } A = \frac{\text{distance } OP}{\text{ordinate of } P} = \frac{d}{y}.$$

Students should observe that continued rotation of OP beyond 360° will give no new position of terminal sides, hence no new functional values. This idea is used in Chapter VI.

In an abbreviated form the functions of the angle A are written:

$$\sin A = \frac{y}{d}. \qquad \tan A = \frac{y}{x}. \qquad \sec A = \frac{d}{x}.$$

$$\cos A = \frac{x}{d}. \qquad \cot A = \frac{x}{y}. \qquad \csc A = \frac{d}{y}.$$

9. Functions of an acute angle of a right triangle

The definitions of the functions of angles of any size will now be applied to the functions of the acute angle of a right triangle. Many problems and exercises exist in which it is necessary to find the unknown parts of a right triangle. For this reason it is convenient to have a different terminology for the functions of an acute angle of the right triangle.

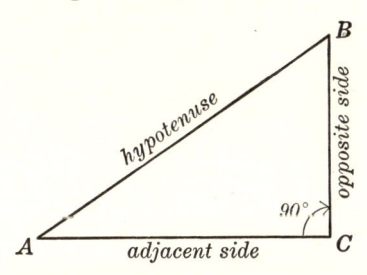

In the right triangle ABC, with the right angle at C, the side CB is the *opposite side* and the side AC is the *adjacent side*. The *hypotenuse* of the right triangle is AB. The functions of the acute angle A of the right triangle ABC are defined as follows:

$$\sin A = \frac{\text{opposite side}}{\text{hypotenuse}}. \qquad \cos A = \frac{\text{adjacent side}}{\text{hypotenuse}}.$$

$$\tan A = \frac{\text{opposite side}}{\text{adjacent side}}. \qquad \cot A = \frac{\text{adjacent side}}{\text{opposite side}}.$$

$$\sec A = \frac{\text{hypotenuse}}{\text{adjacent side}}. \qquad \csc A = \frac{\text{hypotenuse}}{\text{opposite side}}.$$

EXAMPLES

1. The sides of a right triangle are 3, 4, and 5. Find the functions of the acute angle opposite the side 3.

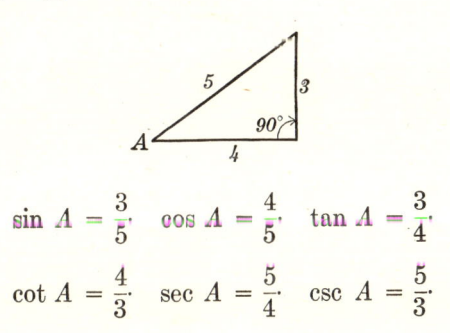

$$\sin A = \frac{3}{5}. \quad \cos A = \frac{4}{5}. \quad \tan A = \frac{3}{4}.$$

$$\cot A = \frac{4}{3}. \quad \sec A = \frac{5}{4}. \quad \csc A = \frac{5}{3}.$$

2. The sides of a right triangle are 5, 12, and 13. Find the functions of the acute angle opposite the side 5.

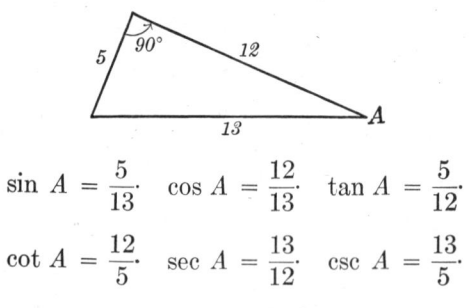

$$\sin A = \frac{5}{13}. \quad \cos A = \frac{12}{13}. \quad \tan A = \frac{5}{12}.$$

$$\cot A = \frac{12}{5}. \quad \sec A = \frac{13}{12}. \quad \csc A = \frac{13}{5}.$$

EXERCISES

1. For the right triangle, figure (*a*), write the six functions of each acute angle of the triangle.

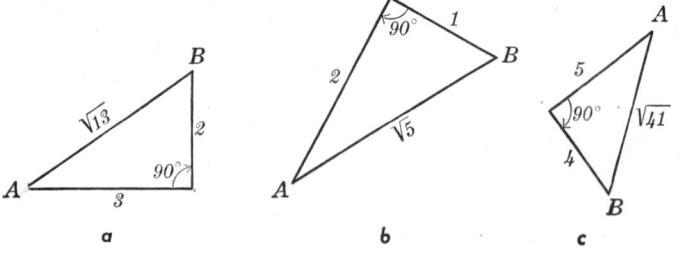

a *b* *c*

2. Repeat exercise (1) but use figure (*b*).
3. Repeat exercise (1) but use figure (*c*).

10. Scale triangle or triangle of reference

A scale triangle for an angle A is a convenient right triangle for use in determining values of the functions of the angle A.

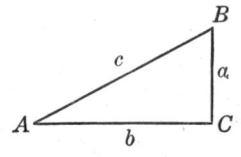

With two of the sides of the triangle chosen so that a given function of angle A will have a given value, the scale triangle may be constructed. The length of the third side is then determined by the relation $a^2 + b^2 = c^2$.

In lettering any triangle, the angles are designated by capital letters, and the side opposite an angle is designated by the corresponding small letter. For example, in the triangle ABC the

RATIOS INVOLVING THE SIDES OF A RIGHT TRIANGLE

side a is opposite angle A, the side b is opposite angle B, and the side c is opposite angle C.

When we wish to construct a scale triangle having two of the functions as sides, choose $a = 1$, or $b = 1$, or $c = 1$, as indicated in the figures below.

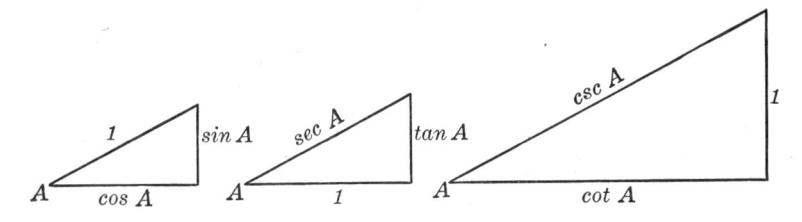

Observe that these triangles are similar to each other. In certain exercises a more convenient scale triangle may be constructed; the plan of construction is shown in the following examples.

EXAMPLES

1. When $\sin A = \frac{5}{13}$, construct the acute angle and write the other functions of angle A.

The given function tells us that for a scale triangle the side opposite angle A is 5 and the hypotenuse is 13. Construct a scale triangle.

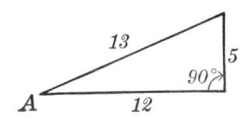

By measurement the side adjacent to angle A is found to be 12. Also by the theorem of Pythagoras we can find that the value of the side adjacent to angle A is 12.

2. When $\cot A = 2$, construct a scale triangle and write the other functions of angle A.

The given function tells us that for a scale triangle the side adjacent to the angle A is 2 and the side opposite is 1. Construct such a scale triangle. The hypotenuse is determined, and by the theorem of Pythagoras we find that its value is $\sqrt{5}$.

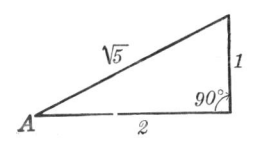

3. In the right triangle ACB the side $a = 9$, and $\sin A = \frac{3}{5}$. Find the hypotenuse and the side b.

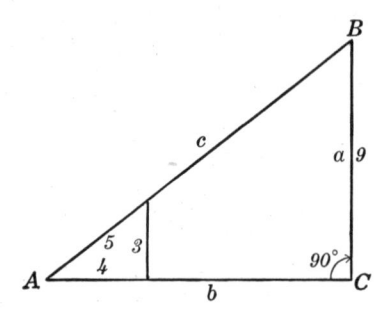

Construct a scale triangle with sides 3, 4, and 5. Since the functions are constant for a given angle, then

$$\frac{a}{c} = \frac{3}{5}, \text{ or } \frac{9}{c} = \frac{3}{5}. \quad c = 15.$$

$$\frac{b}{a} = \frac{4}{3}, \text{ or } \frac{b}{9} = \frac{4}{3}. \quad b = 12.$$

EXERCISES

Construct a scale triangle in each of the following exercises, and write the other functions of the angle.

1. $\cos A = \frac{5}{13}$.
2. $\tan A = \frac{24}{7}$.
3. $\cos A = \frac{8}{17}$.
4. $\sin A = .4 = \frac{4}{10}$.
5. $\cot A = \frac{4}{3}$.
6. $\sec A = \frac{25}{24}$.
7. $\sin A = m$.
8. $\tan A = n$.

For each triangle ACB construct a scale triangle. Write the other functions of the given angle. Find the indicated sides.

9. $\cos A = \frac{4}{7}$ and $c = 21$. Find a and b.
10. $\sin A = \frac{6}{11}$ and $a = 18$. Find b and c.
11. $\tan A = \frac{3}{4}$ and $b = 12$. Find a and c.

11. Functions of 30°, 45°, and 60°

Since the functions of 30°, 45°, and 60° are needed to solve many problems and exercises, it is important that we find their values in terms of rational numbers and surds.

Functions of 45°. In the right isosceles triangle ACB let $a = b = 1$. Then $c = \sqrt{2}$.

RATIOS INVOLVING THE SIDES OF A RIGHT TRIANGLE

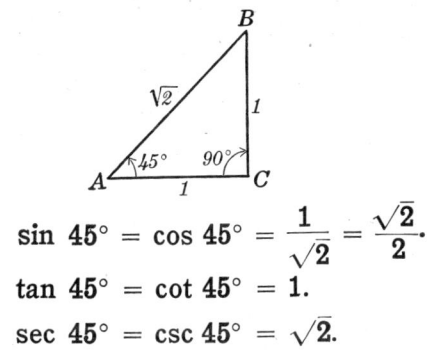

$$\sin 45° = \cos 45° = \frac{1}{\sqrt{2}} = \frac{\sqrt{2}}{2}.$$
$$\tan 45° = \cot 45° = 1.$$
$$\sec 45° = \csc 45° = \sqrt{2}.$$

Functions of 30° and 60°. In a 30°—60° right triangle the hypotenuse is double the shorter side. Let the hypotenuse be 2; then the shorter side is 1, and the longer side is $\sqrt{3}$.

$$\sin 30° = \frac{1}{2}. \qquad \sin 60° = \frac{\sqrt{3}}{2}.$$

$$\cos 30° = \frac{\sqrt{3}}{2}. \qquad \cos 60° = \frac{1}{2}.$$

$$\tan 30° = \frac{1}{\sqrt{3}}. \qquad \tan 60° = \sqrt{3}.$$

$$\cot 30° = \sqrt{3}. \qquad \cot 60° = \frac{1}{\sqrt{3}}.$$

$$\sec 30° = \frac{2}{\sqrt{3}}. \qquad \sec 60° = 2.$$

$$\csc 30° = 2. \qquad \csc 60° = \frac{2}{\sqrt{3}}.$$

In Chapter V much use is made of the functions of 30°, 45°, and 60° in verifying the relations that exist between the functions of other angles, and in solving equations.

EXERCISES

Simplify each exercise.

1. $4 \sin 30° - 8 \tan 45° + 10 \cos 60°$.
Hint: $4 \times (\frac{1}{2}) - 8 \times (1) + 10 \times (\frac{1}{2}) = -1$.

2. $20 \cos^2 60° - 5 \cos^2 30° + 2 \cot 45°$. [$\cos^2 60° = (\cos 60°)^2$].

3. $\sqrt{6} \sin 45° \sin 60° - 4 \sin^2 30°$.
4. $\cos^3 30° + \tan^3 60°$.
5. $4 \tan^2 45° + \sin^3 30° + 16\sqrt{3} \sin 60°$.

12. Variation of the trigonometric functions as the angle increases from 0° to 90°

With a radius of 10 centimeters draw a quadrant AOB of a circle. Draw radii marking off angles at intervals of 5°. From the extremities of the radii draw perpendiculars to OA. The figure then shows a series of right triangles from which the functions of the angles AOB_1, AOB_2, etc., can be computed.

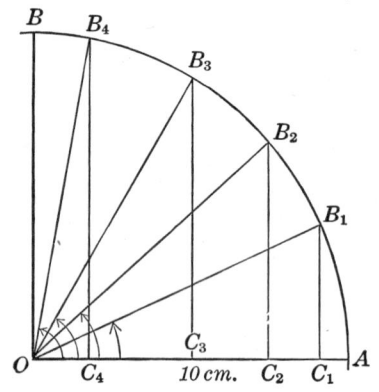

The figure illustrates the general plan of construction.

Make a table like the one below and fill in the values of the functions to the nearest hundredth as determined by measurement and computation.

The values of sin 0°, cos 0°, tan 0°, and sin 90°, cos 90°, and cot 90° are found from the definitions on page 24. It is customary

	0°	20°	35°	55°	65°	75°	80°	85°	90°
sin	0								1
cos	1								0
tan	0								∞
cot	∞								0

RATIOS INVOLVING THE SIDES OF A RIGHT TRIANGLE

to say that tan 90° and cot 0° which have a denominator zero are *not* defined. We say loosely that tan 90° is infinity, and cot 0° is infinity.

From the figure and the table it is evident that as the angle increases from 0° to 90°:

(1) The sine *increases* from 0 to 1.
(2) The cosine *decreases* from 1 to 0.
(3) The tangent *increases* from 0 to larger and larger numbers, and as the angle approaches 90°, the tangent increases without bound; this fact is expressed by saying that tan 90° is *infinity*. The cotangent decreases from infinity to 0.

Note: The symbol for *infinity* is ∞.

13. How to use the table of trigonometric functions

You have just learned how to find the value of a trigonometric function of an acute angle by drawing a scale right triangle and then finding the ratios of the sides in pairs. We will need values of the functions to a higher degree of accuracy. By the use of higher mathematics the values of the functions have been computed. In the table on page 164 are found the values of the sines, cosines, tangents, and cotangents of each angle from 0° to 90°. It is not necessary to use the secant and cosecant of an angle in this chapter. The four-place table gives sufficient accuracy for the computations needed in this book.

For finding the functions of angles of 0° to 45° use the function name at the top of the column, and for angles from 46° to 90° use the function name at the bottom of the column.

Examples

1. Find the value of sin 18°.

See table, page 164.

Find 18° in the angle column. To the right and in the sine column find .3090.

2. Find the value of tan 42°.

Find 42° in the angle column. To the right and in the tangent column find .9004.

3. Find the value of tan 63°.

In the angle column at the right of the table find 63°. To the left and in the column with tan A at the bottom find 1.9626.

4. Find the sin 75°.

Find 75° in the angle column at the right of the table. To the left in the column with sin A at the bottom find .9659.

EXERCISES

Verify the following values.

1. sin 26° = .4384.
2. cos 55° = .5736.
3. tan 28° = .5317.
4. cot 66° = .4452.

5. cos 40° = .7660.
6. sin 84° = .9945.
7. tan 47° = 1.0724.
8. cot 25° = 2.1445.

14. How to find the sine and tangent of an angle involving minutes

EXAMPLES

1. Find sin 24° 25'.

The given angle is between 24° and 25°.
See table on page 164.
Opposite 25° (to the right) in the sine column find .4226
Opposite 24° find .4067
difference .0159

Assume that the change in the angle makes an approximately corresponding change in the function. Then the correction for 25' is ($\frac{25}{60}$ of .0159), which equals .0066. Since the sine function increases as the angle increases, add this correction to the sine of 24°. .4067 + .0066 = .4133.

sin 24° 25' = .4133.

2. Find tan 48° 18'.

The given angle is between 48° and 49°.
See table on page 164.
Read up the column which has the word tangent at the bottom.
Opposite 49° (to the left) in the tangent column find 1.1504
Opposite 48° find 1.1106
difference .0398

Add $\frac{18}{60}$ of .0398 to the tangent of 48°.
1.1106 + .0119 = 1.1225.
tan 48° 18' = 1.1225.

Note: Observe that the *correction is added* when finding the *sine* or *tangent* of an angle involving minutes.

RATIOS INVOLVING THE SIDES OF A RIGHT TRIANGLE

EXERCISES

Verify the following values.
1. sin 37° 28′ = .6083.
2. sin 49° 52′ = .7645.
3. tan 18° 24′ = .3327.
4. tan 65° 17′ = 2.1733.

($\frac{28}{60}$ of 139 = 65).
($\frac{52}{60}$ of 113 = 98).
($\frac{24}{60}$ of 194 = 78).
($\frac{17}{60}$ of 1015 = 288).

15. How to find the cosine and cotangent of an angle involving minutes

EXAMPLES

1. Find cos 35° 28′.
The given angle is between 35° and 36°.
See table on page 164.
Opposite 35° (to the right) in cosine column find .8192
Opposite 36° (to the right) in cosine column find .8090
difference .0102

The correction for 28′ is ($\frac{28}{60}$ of .0102) or .0048. Since the cosine function decreases as the angle increases, *subtract* this correction from the cosine of 35°.
cos 35° 28′ = .8192 − .0048 = .8144.

2. Find cot 58° 22′.
The given angle is between 58° and 59°.
See table on page 164.
Opposite 58° (to the left) in cotangent column find .6249
Opposite 59° (to the left) in cotangent column find .6009
difference .0240

cot 58° 22′ = .6249 − ($\frac{22}{60}$ of .0240) = .6161.

Note: Observe that the *correction is subtracted* when finding the *cosine* or *cotangent* of an angle involving minutes.

EXERCISES

Verify the following values.
1. cos 62° 20′ = .4643.
2. cos 17° 45′ = .9524.
3. cot 32° 54′ = 1.5459.
4. cot 72° 12′ = .3211.

($\frac{20}{60}$ of 155 = 52).
($\frac{45}{60}$ of 52 = 39).
($\frac{54}{60}$ of 604 = 544).
($\frac{12}{60}$ of 192 = 38).

16. Given a function of an angle, to find the angle

EXAMPLES

1. Sin $A = .6324$; find A. See table on page 164.
Reading down the sine column, we observe that .6324 is between .6293 and .6428.

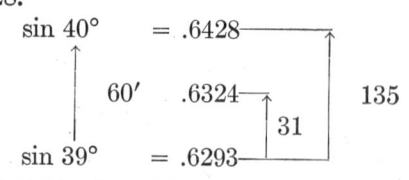

$$
\begin{array}{lll}
\sin 40° & = .6428 \\
\quad 60' & .6324 & 135 \\
& & 31 \\
\sin 39° & = .6293
\end{array}
$$

A difference of 135 in the table makes a difference of 60′ in the angle. Then a difference of 31 in the table will make a difference of $\frac{31}{135}$ of 60′ in the angle. $\frac{31}{135}$ of 60′ = 14′. Then $A = 39° 14'$.

2. Tan $A = 1.2485$; find A. See table on page 164.
Reading up the column having the word tangent at the bottom, we observe that 1.2485 is between 1.2349 and 1.2799.

$$
\begin{array}{lll}
\tan 52° & = 1.2799 \\
\quad 60' & 1.2485 & 450 \\
& & 136 \\
\tan 51° & = 1.2349
\end{array}
$$

$A = 51° + (\frac{136}{450}$ of $60') = 51° 18'$.

EXERCISES

Verify that the following angles correspond to the given functional values.

1. $\sin A = .4623$. $A = 27° 32'$. $(\frac{83}{155}$ of $60' = 32')$.
2. $\sin A = .7841$. $A = 51° 39'$. $(\frac{70}{109}$ of $60' = 39')$.
3. $\tan A = 0.3460$. $A = 19° 5'$. $(\frac{17}{197}$ of $60' = 5')$.
4. $\tan A = 2.4100$. $A = 67° 27'$. $(\frac{541}{1192}$ of $60' = 27')$.

EXAMPLES

1. Cos $A = .7800$; find A. See table on page 164.
Reading down the cosine column, observe that .7800 is between .7880 and .7771.

$$
\begin{array}{lll}
\cos 39° & = .7771 \\
\quad 60' & .7800 & 109 \\
& & 80 \\
\cos 38° & = .7880
\end{array}
$$

$A = 38° + (\frac{80}{109}$ of $60') = 38° 44'$.

RATIOS INVOLVING THE SIDES OF A RIGHT TRIANGLE 35

2. Cot $A = .4900$; find A. See table on page 164.
Reading up the column which has the word cotangent at the bottom, observe that .4900 is between .5095 and .4877.

```
    cot 64°    = .4877 ─┐
                         │
         60'   .4900 ─┐  │  218
                      │195│
                      │   │
    cot 63°    = .5095─┴──┘
```

$A = 63° + (\frac{195}{218}$ of $60') = 63° 54'$.

EXERCISES

Verify the following angles.
1. $\cos A = .4632$. $A = 62° 24'$. ($\frac{63}{155}$ of $60' = 24'$).
2. $\cos A = .8491$. $A = 31° 53'$. ($\frac{81}{92}$ of $60' = 53'$).
3. $\cot A = 1.2486$. $A = 38° 42'$. ($\frac{313}{450}$ of $60' = 42'$).
4. $\cot A = 0.6215$. $A = 58° 9'$. ($\frac{34}{240}$ of $60' = 9'$).

EXERCISES IN EVALUATING FORMULAS THAT INVOLVE TRIGONOMETRIC FUNCTIONS

1. When light passes from one medium to another, as from air through a glass plate with parallel faces, the number of degrees in the angles of incidence and refraction I and R are connected by the formula

$$\sin R = k \sin I,$$

where k is a constant, known as the *index of refraction*. Find R when $k = 1.6$ and $I = 35° 20'$.

2. If a light of C candle power is hung h feet above a horizontal surface, the intensity (I) of illumination at a point on the surface which is R feet from a point directly below the light is expressed by the formula

$$I = \frac{C \cos^3 A}{h^2}.$$

A is the angle at the light whose tangent is $\frac{R}{h}$. Find I when $C = 300$, $A = 60°$, and $h = 10$. $\cos^3 A = (\cos A)^3$.

3. The formula for the number (V) of feet per second in the velocity of an object sliding down a board a distance of d feet inclined at an angle A with the horizontal is

$$V = \sqrt{2 \, gd \sin A};$$

g is a constant which equals approximately 32, the number of feet per sec. per sec. in the acceleration due to gravity. Frictional resistance is neglected. Find V when $d = 100$ and $A = 32° 45'$.

4. If an object in a vacuum is thrown at an angle of A degrees with the horizontal and has an initial velocity of V_1 feet per second, the range (R feet) is expressed by the formula

$$R = \frac{2\,V_1^2 \sin A \cos A}{g}.$$

Find R when $A = 65°$ and $V_1 = 50$, assuming $g = 32$.

5. If an aviator wishes to take the shortest route from one point on the earth's surface to another point, he follows the path of a great circle on the earth's surface. If the latitude and the longitude of the two places are known, he can find the great circle distance between them. The formula is

$$\cos X = \sin L_1 \sin L_2 + \cos L_1 \cos L_2 \cos D.$$

X = number of degrees in the great circle distance between the two places.
L_1 = number of degrees in the latitude of one place.
L_2 = number of degrees in the latitude of the second place.
D = number of degrees in the difference of the longitudes.

1° in circular measure on earth's surface is approximately 69.1 statute or geographical miles.

Find the great circle distance from New York City to San Francisco. San Francisco is 38° north latitude, 122° 30′ west longitude; New York City is 39° 45′ north latitude and 74° west longitude.

Note: The formula applies directly only if the two places are on the same side of the equator.

6. A board plank is inclined at an angle of A degrees to the horizontal. In the study of the motion of objects, it is known that a force of P pounds is required to move a weight of W pounds up the plane. The constant coefficient of friction is k. The formula is

$$P = W\,\frac{\sin A + k \sin A}{\cos A - k \sin A}.$$

Find the value of P when the weight is 1000 lb., $A = 30°$, $k = .1$.

7. For the greatest range of a ball, it should be started in its path in a direction of $A = 45°$ with the horizontal. Considering

RATIOS INVOLVING THE SIDES OF A RIGHT TRIANGLE 37

only the resulting action of gravity, the equation of its path is

$$y = x \tan A - \frac{32x^2}{2V_1^2 \cos^2 A}.$$

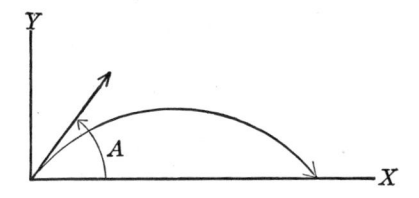

Find the greatest range when the initial velocity is 100 (V_1) feet per second. *Hint:* $y = 0$ when the ball hits the ground.

REVIEW QUESTIONS ON CHAPTER II

1. Name and define the six functions of an angle studied in this chapter.

2. Give from memory the sine, cosine, and tangent of 0°, 30°, 45°, 60°, and 90°.

3. Show by a drawing how the sine, cosine, and tangent of an angle change as the angle increases from 0° to 90°.

4. Given $\sin A = \frac{5}{13}$, construct a scale triangle and write the other functions of angle A.

5. Given $\tan A = \frac{7}{24}$, construct a scale triangle. If side $b = 96$, find sides a and c. Write the other functions of angle A.

6. The base of an isosceles triangle is 40 feet, and the angle at the vertex is 70°. Determine the altitude of the triangle and the lengths of the equal sides.

7. Two buildings of equal heights are opposite each other and on opposite sides of a street 120 feet wide. From a point in the street the angles of elevation of the tops of the buildings are 65° and 40°. How high are the buildings? How far is the point of observation from the base of each building?

8. Using the tables, find the following functions: sin 28° 40′; sin 61° 35′; tan 20° 25′; tan 72° 42′; cos 12° 24′; cos 54° 18′; cot 40° 20′; cot 50° 15′.

9. Using the tables, find the angles for the following functions:

$\sin A = .4444.$ $\cos A = .9002.$
$\sin A = .7540.$ $\cos A = .6286.$
$\tan A = .3261.$ $\cot A = 3.5624.$
$\tan A = 1.8562.$ $\cot A = .7436.$

The Origin of the Names of the Trigonometric Functions

THE six functions of the angle about which you have learned were developed in man's attempt to solve the triangle. During the centuries different names have been used to designate the functions. Mention will be made only of the modern terms. The term *sine* is the oldest of these.

Referring to the Hindu word for half chord, Dr. Vera Sanford says: "Arab translators made this into the word *gib* which because of its similarity in sound to their word for 'fold' or 'bay' confused the two meanings, or at least drew no distinction between them. Accordingly the word was translated into Latin as 'sinus' (a fold) and later it became sine." The use of the term "sinus" probably dates back to the twelfth century.

The historian Cajori says that we doubtless owe to Thomas Finck, a native of Schleswig-Holstein, the beginning of the use in 1583 of the words *tangent* and *secant* as names for trigonometric functions. The reasons for the choice of these terms is evident from the following figure:

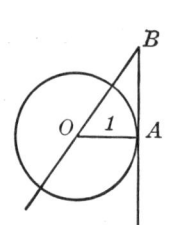

Draw a circle with radius OA equal to 1 unit.

$$\tan AOB = \frac{AB}{OA} = \frac{AB}{1} = AB.$$

AB is a *tangent* to the circle.

$$\sec AOB = \frac{OB}{OA} = \frac{OB}{1} = OB.$$

OB produced through O is a *secant* of the circle.

The terms *cosine* and *cotangent* were coined by the Englishman Gunter (1620) out of the expressions "sine of the complement" or "complemental sine," and "tangent of the complement" or "complemental tangent." Similarly the word *cosecant* can be accounted for.

CHAPTER

III

Solving Right Triangles

~~~~~~~

THE trigonometric functions which have been presented in Chapter II have many practical applications. In this chapter we shall learn to use these functions to find parts of a right triangle.

Every right triangle has three sides and three angles, which will be called its parts. It is possible to find all the other parts when three parts are given, if one of the given parts is a side. Finding the unknown parts is called *solving a right triangle*.

Two cases arise in the solution of right triangles:

      Case I. Given one side and one acute angle.

      Case II. Given two sides.

In each case the third given part is the right angle.

17. Suggestions for a plan of solution

1. Write the given data and state the required parts.
2. From the given data construct a scale drawing which is to be used as a check on the computation.
3. Write the formulas needed for the computation.
4. Use values of functions given in the table on page 104.
5. Remember that $A + B = 90°$, A and B being the acute angles of the right triangle.
6. Compute the angles to the nearest minute.
7. Compute the sides to the nearest second decimal figure, unless otherwise specified.
8. *Arithmetical check:* $a^2 + b^2 = c^2$ or
$$a^2 = (c - b)(c + b).$$

Examples

1. Given $a = 3$, $b = 4$, find c, A, and B.

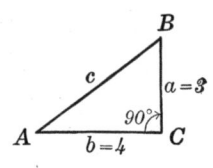

Formulas:
$$\tan A = \frac{a}{b}.$$
$$c^2 = a^2 + b^2.$$
$$B = 90° - A.$$

Computation:
$\tan A = \frac{3}{4} = .7500$; hence $A = 36° \; 52'$, $B = 53° \; 8'$.
$c^2 = 3^2 + 4^2 = 25$; then $c = 5$.

2. Given $b = 8$, $A = 46° \; 30'$, find a, c, and B.

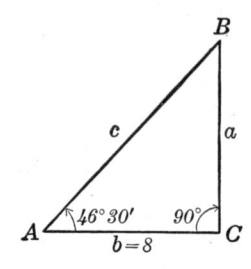

Formulas:
$$B = 90° - A.$$
$$\frac{a}{b} = \tan A \text{ or } a = b \tan A.$$
$$\frac{b}{c} = \cos A \text{ or } c = \frac{b}{\cos A}.$$
Check: $a^2 = c^2 - b^2$.

Computation:
$B = 90° - 46° \; 30' = 43° \; 30'$.
$a = 8 \tan 46° \; 30' = 8 \times 1.0540 = 8.43$.
$c = \dfrac{8}{\cos 46° \; 30'} = \dfrac{8}{.6883} = 11.62$.
Check: $8.43^2 = 3.62 \times 19.62$.
$71.06 = 71.02$ (approximately).

EXERCISES

Solve the right triangles.
1. $A = 30°$, $a = 12$ (Orally).
2. $A = 45°$, $c = 10$ (Orally).

SOLVING RIGHT TRIANGLES

3. $A = 28°, b = 14$.
4. $B = 55° 30', c = 28.4$.
5. $B = 18°, a = 16$.
6. $a = 36, b = 72$.

7. $a = 7, c = 25$.
8. $b = 10, c = 26$.
9. $A = 61° 42', c = 25$.
10. $B = 32° 18', a = 12$.

11. The angle of elevation of a kite is measured and found to be 52°. The length of the kite string is known to be 500 feet. Assuming the line of the string to be straight, find the height of the kite.

12. A post 10 feet high standing vertically on level ground casts a shadow of 8.5 feet. Find the angle of elevation of the sun.

13. To find the distance across a lake, two trees M and N on opposite sides are marked. At M a line is laid off at right angles to MN and continued a distance of 700 feet to R. The angle MRN is found to be 68°. Find the distance across the lake.

14. A straight road rises 1 foot for every 30 feet measured along the road. Find the angle which the road makes with the horizontal.

15. From a window in a lighthouse which is 105.4 feet above the level of a lake a small object is seen floating on the water. Its angle of depression is found to be 23° 18'. What is the distance of the object from the lighthouse?

16. In a circle of radius 12 inches find the number of degrees in a central angle subtended by a chord 8 inches in length.

17. A person at point A sees an inaccessible object due south at point B. He walks in a direction 40° east of south for a distance of 800 feet and then observes that the object is due west. Find his original distance from the object.

18. An engineer living in an apartment house wishes to know the height of a hotel across the street. From his window ledge, which he knows is 35 feet above street level, he finds the angle of depression of the base of the hotel to be 24° and the angle of elevation of its top to be 65°. What is the height of the hotel?

19. From a point 28.4 feet high on top of a building a radio aerial is stretched to the top of a pole 48.6 feet high. The horizontal distance from the point on the building to the pole is 64.8 feet. Find the number of degrees in the angle which the aerial makes with the horizontal.

20. A straight tunnel runs through a mountain in an east-to-west direction. At the east entrance the angle of depression is 5°, and the oblique distance through the tunnel is 800 feet. How far is the west entrance below the east entrance?

21. A vein of coal has an inclination of 35°, and a horizontal width of $10\frac{3}{4}$ feet where it comes out on level surface. What is the thickness of the vein of coal?

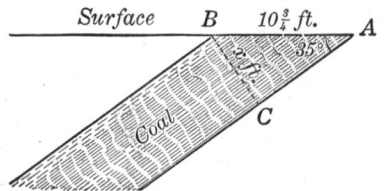

22. See figure for problem 21. A vertical shaft is sunk 1000 feet west of point A. In order to reach the vein of coal, how deep must the shaft be?

23. Prove that the distance around the earth at a latitude of 60° is equal to half the length of the equator.

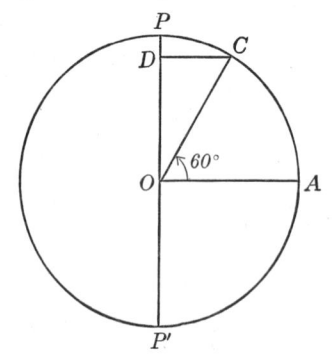

Suggestion: The figure represents a section through the center of the earth, P and P' being the poles. C is the point on the earth's surface having a latitude of 60°, and A is a point on the equator with its radius OA. CD is the radius of the circle at the 60° parallel. Let $OA = OC = R$. Then $CD = R \sin 30° = R \cos 60°$.

24. See figure for problem 23. (a) Find the distance around the earth on the 45° parallel of latitude. (b) Find the approximate velocity, due to the rotation of the earth, of a point on the 45° parallel. Use 8000 miles as the diameter of the earth. (c) How much longer is a degree of longitude at the 45° parallel than at the 60° parallel?

25. In an isosceles triangle the equal sides are each 59 inches and the equal base angles are 42°. Solve the triangle and find the area.

26. A rectangle is 12 inches wide and 15 inches long. Find the angles between the diagonals.

27. The diagonals of a rhombus are 36 inches and 48 inches. Find the angles of the rhombus and the length of each side. *Hint:* The sides of a rhombus are equal, and the diagonals are perpendicular to each other.

SOLVING RIGHT TRIANGLES

28. In a circle of radius 8 feet is a chord of length 5 feet. Find the angle subtended at the center by the chord.

29. A pendulum 36 inches long is moved 10° from the vertical. The lower end of the pendulum is lifted through what distance?

30. The side of a regular decagon is 12 inches. Find the area of the decagon and the radii of the inscribed and circumscribed circles.

31. A tree is standing at the edge of a pool of clear water. From a point 10 feet above the water the angle of elevation of the top of the tree is 45°. The angle of depression of the lowest point of the image is 60°. The angle of refraction is neglected. The length of the image appears to be the same length as the height of the tree. Find the height of the tree. See figure for problem 4, page 9.

32. When the sun's rays were inclined 40° to the horizontal, the shadow of a tower measured 160 feet in length. Also a flagpole on top of the tower made a shadow 62 feet long. What is the height of the tower and the length of the flagpole?

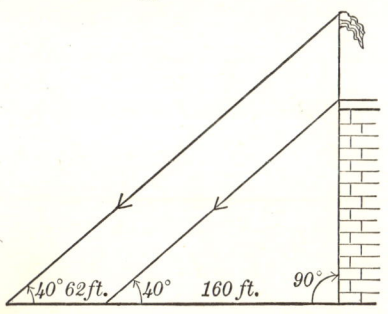

33. The sides of a triangle are 24 inches, 30 inches, and 36 inches. Find the angles of the triangle.

Hint: Let the altitude to the 36-inch side be y inches. The foot of this perpendicular line divides the 36-inch side into parts of x inches and $(36 - x)$ inches. Use the theorem of Pythagoras; then solve the two resulting equations for x.

34. An airplane was flying due west at 90 miles per hour. At noon the pilot observed a signal tower to be N. 25° E. At 12:20 o'clock the direction of the tower was N. 60° E. Determine when the airplane was nearest the tower and its distance from the tower.

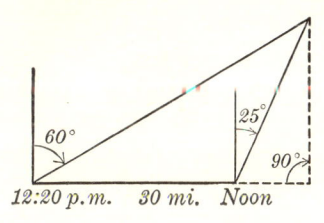

35. The top of a mountain is known to be 1200 feet higher than two points (A and B) on opposite sides of the mountain. At point A the angle of elevation of the top is 35°, and at B the angle of elevation of the top is 50°. Find the length of a tunnel from A to B.

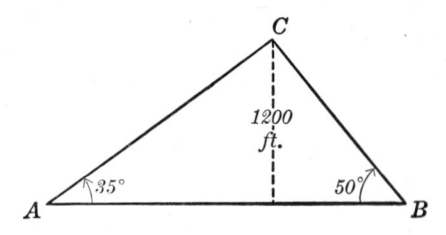

36. At a given point from the base of a tree the angle of elevation of the top of the tree is angle A. At a distance of d feet farther away from the base of the tree the angle of elevation of the top of the tree is angle B. Show that the number of feet in the height of the tree is expressed by the formula

$$h = \frac{d \tan A \tan B}{\tan A - \tan B}.$$

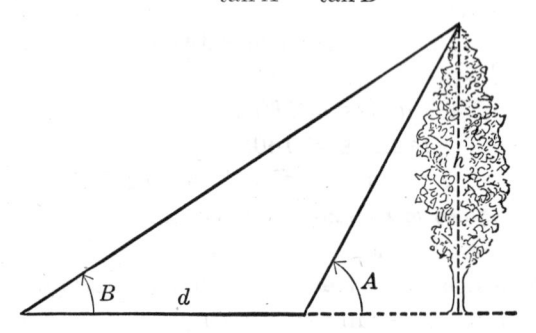

37. From the top of a mountain the angles of depression of two successive milestones (on the same side of the mountain) are 5° and 10°. Find the height of the mountain. Use the formula of problem 36.

18. Radian measure of angles

Meaning of a radian. In Chapter I you learned about the degree-measure of angles, the unit being one-ninetieth of a right angle. In most types of applications involving the solving of triangles the degree is used. However, in certain types of problems it is more convenient to consider angles measured by a unit called a *radian*.

SOLVING RIGHT TRIANGLES

A radian is an angle which if placed with its vertex at the center of a circle intercepts an arc equal in length to the radius of the circle.

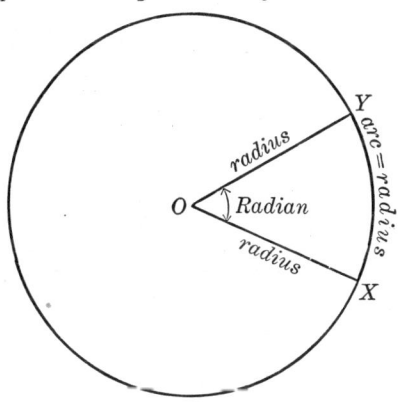

Angle $XOY = 1$ radian.

Radians and degrees. Since the circumference of a circle is equal to 2π times the radius, it follows that the circumference subtends an angle of 2π radians at the center of the circle. Also we know that the circumference subtends an angle of 360° at the center. Then

2π radians $= 360°$.
π radians $= 180°$.
1 radian $= 57°\ 17'\ 45''$ or $57.3°$.

Changing degrees to radians. To change degrees to radians, divide the number of degrees by 57.3.

Changing radians to degrees. To change radians to degrees, multiply 57.3° by the number of radians.

Notation for angles. The symbol π (pi) may have different meanings. When π denotes a number, it means approximately 3.14 or $3\frac{1}{7}$. When π denotes an angle, it means π radians, or 180°. Generally, the word *radian* is omitted. Thus, $\pi = 180°$, $\frac{\pi}{2} = 90°, \frac{\pi}{3} = 60°, \frac{3\pi}{4} = 135°$. We shall use A_r to denote the number of radians in angle A.

EXERCISES

1. Express in degrees: 2 radians; 5 radians; $\frac{1}{2}$ radian; .45 radian; 2.56 radians; 7 radians; 10 radians.

2. Draw the following angles: $\frac{\pi}{2}; \frac{\pi}{4}; \frac{\pi}{6}; \frac{2\pi}{3}$.

3. Express in radians: 15°; 20°; 30°; 45°; 60°; 75°; 90°; 120°; 135°; 180°; 225°.

4. Express in radians, carrying the division to the nearest four-place decimal: 24°; 65°; 80°; 100°; 138°; 176°.

5. Express in radians, carrying the division to the nearest four-place decimal: 18° 30′; 35° 36′; 80° 45′; 112° 17′; 136° 42′; 200° 47′.

6. Express in degrees: $\dfrac{\pi}{4}$; $\dfrac{\pi}{5}$; $\dfrac{\pi}{8}$; $\dfrac{3\pi}{5}$; $\dfrac{5\pi}{12}$; $\dfrac{2\pi}{3}$; $\dfrac{3\pi}{2}$.

7. What is the value of $\sin \dfrac{\pi}{4}$; $\cos \dfrac{\pi}{3}$; $\tan \dfrac{\pi}{4}$; $\sin \dfrac{\pi}{6}$; $\cot \dfrac{\pi}{4}$; $\tan \dfrac{\pi}{3}$; $\cos \dfrac{\pi}{6}$?

19. Three important theorems

The length of an arc of a circle.

Theorem 1. *The number of linear units in the arc of any circle is equal to the product of the number of linear units in the radius and the number of radians in the central angle subtended by the arc.*

Proof: Let s represent the number of linear units in the arc AC. Let R represent the number of linear units in the radius, which would make R the number of linear units in the arc AB. Then

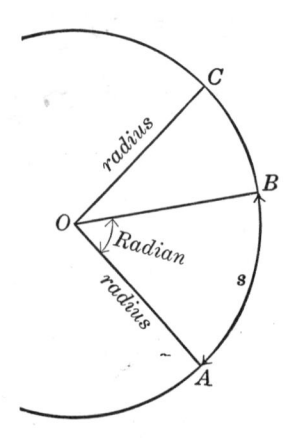

$$\dfrac{s}{R} = \text{the number of radians in angle } AOC.$$

Hence

$s = R$ times the number of radians in angle AOC.

$$s = R \times A_r.$$

SOLVING RIGHT TRIANGLES

Examples

1. In a circle of radius 10 feet an arc subtends an angle of 70° at the center. Find the length of the arc.

$$70° = \frac{70}{57.3} \text{ radians} = 1.2216 \text{ radians}.$$

Note: Express the number of radians to the nearest four-place decimal.

$$s = R \times A_r.$$
$$s = 10 \times 1.2216 = 12.216.$$

The arc is 12.22 feet.

2. A circle has a radius of 20 feet. An arc of 18 feet subtends what central angle in degrees?

From $s = R \times A_r$ we get $A_r = \frac{s}{R}.$

Number of radians in central angle = $\frac{18}{20} = .9$.

.9 radian = $.9 \times 57.3° = 51.57°$.

3. Find the radius of a circle in which an arc of 12 feet subtends a central angle of 36° 15′.

$$36° \ 15' = 36.25 \times \frac{1}{57.3} \text{ radians} = .6326 \text{ radians}.$$

From $s = R \times A_r$ we get $R = \frac{s}{A_r}.$

$$R = \frac{12}{.6326} = 18.97.$$

The radius is 18.97 feet.

EXERCISES

1. The radius of a circle is 8 feet. An arc of 4 feet subtends what angle at the center?

2. The radius of a circle is 10 feet. An arc subtends an angle of 48° 25′. Find the length of the arc.

3. Find the radius of a circle in which an arc of 12 feet subtends an angle of 65° 24′.

4. At what distance does an object 6 feet high subtend an angle of 8′? *Hint:* Assume 6 feet to be the measurement of an arc of a circle of radius R feet.

5. Find the length of a stick which at a distance of one mile will subtend an angle of 2′ at the eye.

6. A tower having a height of 48 feet subtends an angle of 10′ at the eye. How far away is the tower?

7. A railroad track has a rise of 4 feet for a horizontal distance of 700 feet. What is the inclination of the track to the horizontal?

8. The diameter of the moon is about 2160 miles. The moon's diameter subtends an angle of .0090524 radians at the eye. What is the moon's distance from the earth?

9. Assume the distance from the earth to the sun to be 93,000,000 miles. If the sun's diameter subtends an angle of .0093283 radians at the eye, what is the sun's diameter?

10. The radius of the earth is about 3956 miles. An arc of 1° on the equator is how many miles in length?

11. The radii of two drive pulleys are 6 feet and 2 feet respectively, and the distance between the centers of the pulleys is 18 feet. Find the length of an open belt required to go around the pulleys. Make no allowance for the sag of the belt.

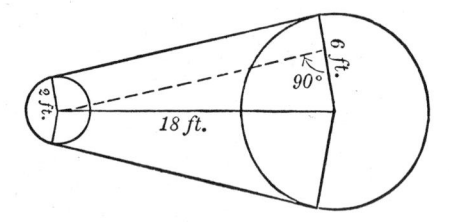

An approximate check is obtained by adding one-half the sum of the two circumferences to twice the distance between the centers.

Area of a sector of a circle.

Theorem 2. *The number of square units in the area of a sector of a circle is equal to one-half the square of the number of linear units in the radius times the number of radians in the angle of the sector.*

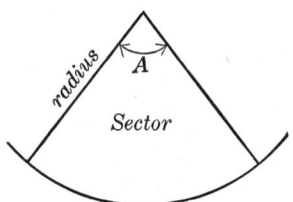

Proof: Let R linear units be the radius of the circle; A_r the number of radians in the angle of the sector; K the number of square units in the area of the sector.

The ratio of the area of the sector to the area of the circle is the same as the ratio of the angle of the sector to 360° or 2π radians.

$$\frac{\text{Area of sector}}{\text{Area of circle}} = \frac{A_r}{2\pi},$$

$$\frac{K}{\pi R^2} = \frac{A_r}{2\pi}.$$

SOLVING RIGHT TRIANGLES

Multiplying each member of the above equation by πR^2 we get
$$K = \tfrac{1}{2} R^2 \times A_r.$$

EXAMPLE

In a circle of radius 20 inches the angle of a sector is 100°. Find the area of the sector.
$$K = \tfrac{1}{2} \times 20^2 \times \frac{100}{57.3} = 349.04.$$

The area of the sector is 349.04 square inches.

Area of a segment of a circle. *Theorem 3. If the radius of the circle is R linear units, and A_r is the number of radians in the angle of the sector, the formula for the area of the segment is*
$$K = \tfrac{1}{2} R^2 (A_r - \sin A).$$

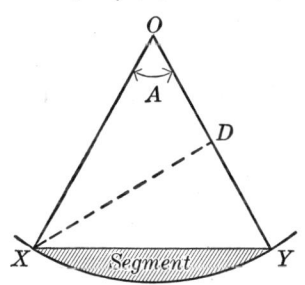

Proof: The line XD is perpendicular to the radius OY. The area of the segment equals the area of the sector XOY minus the area of the triangle XOY.

For the sector XOY: $K_1 = \tfrac{1}{2} R^2 A_r.$
For the triangle XOY: $K_2 = \tfrac{1}{2} OY \times XD.$
$OY = R$, and $XD = R \sin A$.
Then $\quad K_2 = \tfrac{1}{2} R^2 \sin A. \quad K = K_1 - K_2.$
$K = \tfrac{1}{2} R^2 A_r - \tfrac{1}{2} R^2 \sin A.$
$K = \tfrac{1}{2} R^2 (A_r - \sin A).$

Note: If angle A is greater than 90°, for $\sin A$ use the sine of the supplement of angle A. The proof of this fact is given later. Thus if $A = 110°$, $\sin 110° = \sin 70°$.

EXAMPLE

In a circle of radius 4 feet the angle of a segment is 80°. Find the area of the segment.
$$K = \tfrac{1}{2} \times 4^2 \left(\frac{80}{57.3} - \sin 80°\right) = 8(1.3902 - .9848) = 3.2912.$$

The area of the segment is 3.29 square feet.

EXERCISES

1. The radius of a circle is 4 feet. The angle of a sector is 72°. Find the area of the sector and of the corresponding segment.
2. In a circle of radius 10 inches the angle of a sector is 120°. Find the area of the sector, and the corresponding segment.
3. The radius of a circle is 13 inches. A chord is 5 inches from the center of the circle. Find the area of the smaller segment cut off by the chord.
4. A horizontal cylindrical gasoline tank 8 feet long has a diameter of 3 feet. If the tank is filled to a depth of 16 inches, how many gallons of gasoline are in the tank? (Use 1 cu. ft. = $7\frac{1}{2}$ gal.) *Hint:* The number of cubic feet of gasoline equals the number of square feet in the area of a segment of a circle multiplied by the number of feet in the length of the tank.

20. Vectors and vector quantities

A vector is a straight line-segment having a definite length and a specified direction. Some physical quantities can be expressed by a given number of units. The speed of a moving object may be expressed by a number of linear units per unit of time. Such quantities are called *scalar quantities*. Other types of quantities need to be specified more definitely than by so many units. For instance, velocity and acceleration of a moving object have direction as well as magnitude; also a force due to a push or pull. Such quantities are called *vector quantities*, and may be represented by straight line-segments defined as vectors.

If a boat moves northeast with a speed of 12 miles per hour, its speed and direction can be represented by a vector (OA in the vector diagram below).

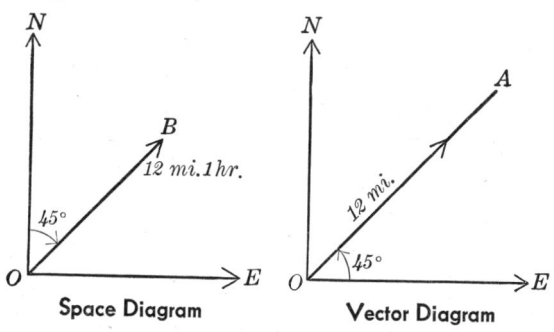

Space Diagram   Vector Diagram

In the space diagram the line OB indicates only the direction

SOLVING RIGHT TRIANGLES

of motion, while in the vector diagram the line-segment OA represents both the direction of motion and the magnitude of the speed. In the vector diagram the vector OA is parallel to OB in the space diagram.

21. Components of a vector quantity

An airplane is moving in a direction of N. 30° E. with a speed of 120 miles an hour. How many miles an hour is the airplane advancing in a due eastward direction? In a due northward direction?

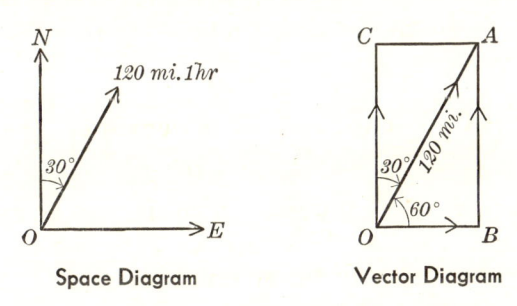

Space Diagram   Vector Diagram

In the vector diagram the vector OB represents the magnitude of the velocity of the airplane in a due eastward direction. The vector OC represents the magnitude of the velocity of the airplane in a due northward direction. The eastward and northward velocities are known as the components of the velocity at which the airplane is actually moving.

From the triangle OBA in the vector diagram,

$OB = OA \cos 60° = 120 \times \frac{1}{2} = 60$. The eastward component is 60 miles an hour.

$OC = BA = OA \sin 60° = 120 \times .866 = 103.92$. The northward component is 103.92 miles an hour.

When the two components of a vector quantity are selected at right angles to each other, the components are called *rectangular components*.

Example

A force of 60 pounds acts at an angle of 35° with the horizontal. What two forces, one acting horizontally, the other acting vertically, would have the same effect?

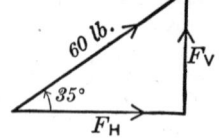

Let F_H represent the number of pounds in the horizontal component, and let F_V represent the number of pounds in the vertical component.
$F_H = 60 \cos 35° = 49.15$.
$F_V = 60 \sin 35° = 34.42$.
The horizontal component is 49.15 pounds, and the vertical component is 34.42 pounds.

EXERCISES

1. A steamer is going northeast at a speed of 24 miles per hour. Find the northern and eastern components of its velocity.

2. A stone is projected at an angle of 40° with the horizontal with a speed of 600 feet per second. Find the horizontal and the vertical component velocities.

3. A vessel is steaming in a direction due north across a current running due west. At the end of two hours the vessel has made 22 miles in a direction 35° west of north. Find the speed of the current and the speed at which the vessel is steaming.

4. An object is moving in a straight line with a speed of 20 feet per second. Find the two rectangular component speeds, one in a direction at an angle of 60° to its direction of motion.

5. A force of 200 pounds is acting in a direction of N. 54° E. Find the eastern and northern components of this force.

6. Two towns A and B are on a road having a direction of N. 40° E. The distance between the towns is 40 miles. B is how many miles east and how many miles north of A?

7. A rod OA 8 feet long is fastened at O. A force of 80 pounds is applied at A and acts at an angle of 30° with OA. Find the moment (turning effect) of the force about the point O.

The moment of a force about a point is equal to the product of the force and the number (d) of linear units in its lever arm. A lever arm means the perpendicular distance from the point (O) to the line of action of the force.

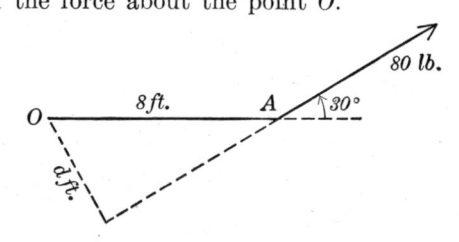

22. Composition of a vector quantity

Two forces acting simultaneously on an object may be replaced by a single force called a *resultant*. In other words, the

SOLVING RIGHT TRIANGLES

resultant will produce the same effect on the object as the joint action of the two forces.

If two vector quantities are represented by the vectors AB and AD, then their resultant will be represented by the vector AC, which is the diagonal of the parallelogram $ABCD$. This principle is known as *the law of the parallelogram of forces*.

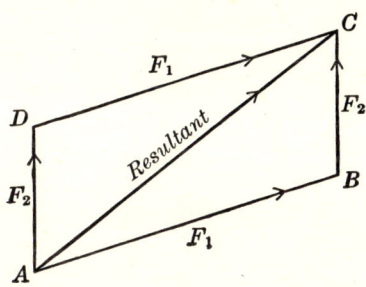

Examples

1. A man walks due northeast at a speed of 3 miles an hour across the deck of a vessel going east at 4 miles an hour. Find the resultant velocity with which the man is moving over the water.

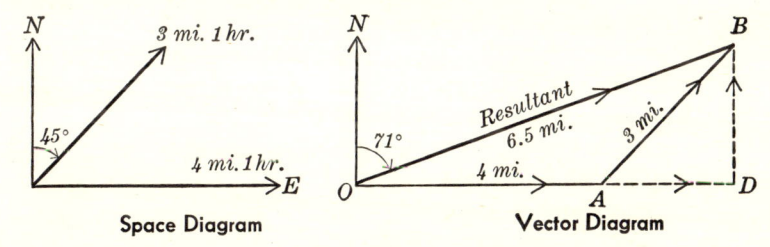

Space Diagram

Vector Diagram

First make a space diagram; then make a vector diagram. In the vector diagram the vector OA represents the magnitude of the velocity of the vessel. The vector AB represents the magnitude and direction of his walking. Then the vector OB represents the magnitude of the resultant velocity.

Computation: Resolve each velocity into eastward and northward components. The combined eastward component is the base OD of the right triangle ODB. The combined northward component is the altitude DB of the same right triangle. The hypotenuse OB of this right triangle represents the magnitude of the resultant velocity R.

$$OD = OA + AD = 4 + 3 \cos 45° = 6.12.$$
$$DB = 3 \sin 45° = 2.12.$$

$$OB = R = \sqrt{(OD)^2 + (DB)^2} = 6.48.$$

$$\tan AOB = \tan DOB = \frac{DB}{OD} = .3464. \quad \angle AOB = 19° 6'.$$

The resultant velocity is 6.48 miles per hour in a direction of N. 70° 54′ E.

Check formula: When two forces or velocities act at an angle A with each other, the formula for the resultant is

$$R^2 = F_1^2 + F_2^2 + 2F_1F_2 \cos A.$$

2. Two forces are represented by the vectors F_1 (12 pounds, 30°) and F_2 (20 pounds, 60°). Find the resultant.

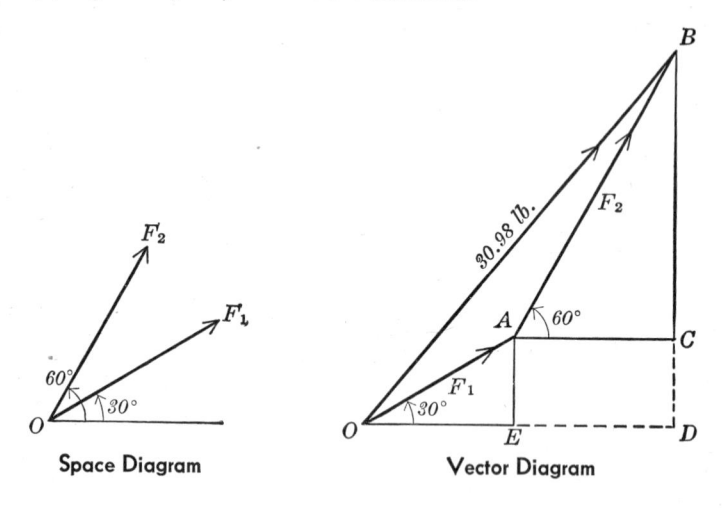

Space Diagram

Vector Diagram

Computation: OA is parallel to OF_1, and AB is parallel to OF_2.

$OD = OE + ED = OE + AC.$
$OD = 12 \cos 30° + 20 \cos 60° = 20.39.$
$DB = DC + CB = EA + CB.$
$DB = 12 \sin 30° + 20 \sin 60° = 23.32.$

$$OB = R = \sqrt{(OD)^2 + (DB)^2} = 30.98.$$

$$\tan DOB = \frac{DB}{OD} = 1.1437.$$

$\angle DOB = 48° 50'.$

The resultant is (30.98 pounds, 48° 50′).
Check: $R^2 = 12^2 + 20^2 + 2 \times 12 \times 20 \times .866 = 959.68.$ $R = 30.98.$

EXERCISES

1. Two forces of 30 pounds and 40 pounds act at right angles to each other. Find the resultant and the angle between the resultant and the 40-pound force.

2. An airship has a speed of 40 miles per hour and is heading due south. The wind is blowing southeast (S. 45° E.) with a speed of 30 miles per hour. Find how far the airship travels in one hour and its direction.

SOLVING THE GENERAL TRIANGLE

Then $\sin A = \dfrac{h}{c}$;

Hence $\dfrac{a}{2R} = \dfrac{h}{c}$,

and $R = \dfrac{ac}{2h}.$ \hfill (2)

We know that $\tfrac{1}{2} bh = K$.

Substituting the value of $h = \dfrac{2K}{b}$ in (2) gives

$$R = \dfrac{abc}{4K}.$$

Example

Find the radius of the circumscribed circle for the triangle when $a = 8$, $b = 12$, and $c = 14$.

$K = \sqrt{s(s - a)(s - b)(s - c)}$. $s = 17$, $s - a = 9$, $s - b = 5$, and $s - c = 3$.

$$R = \dfrac{8 \times 12 \times 14}{4\sqrt{17 \times 9 \times 5 \times 3}} = 7.01.$$

EXERCISES

1. Using the relation (1) on page 70, show how the formula for the *sine theorem* may be developed, that is,

$$2R = \dfrac{a}{\sin A} = \dfrac{b}{\sin B} = \dfrac{c}{\sin C}.$$

2. Find the radii of the inscribed and circumscribed circles for the triangles.

(a) $a = 8$, $b = 10$, $c = 12$.
(b) $a = 8$, $b = 15$, $c = 17$.

3. Find R when
(a) $a = 18$, $A = 50°$.
(b) $a = 40$, $A = 120°$.
(c) $b = 48$, $B = 30°$.
(d) $c = 100$, $C = 42°$.

30. Tangent half-angle theorem

In any triangle the tangent of half of any angle is equal to the quotient of the radius of the inscribed circle divided by the difference between the semi-perimeter of the triangle and the side opposite the specified angle.

Given the three sides of a triangle, find the angles.

We can find the angles by using the *cosine theorem*, but often it is more convenient to use the *tangent half-angle theorem*. In general the tangent half-angle theorem gives more accurate results.

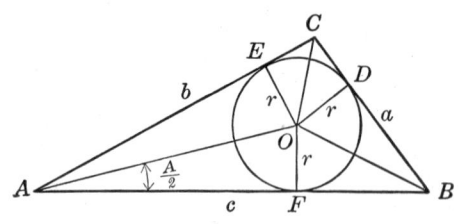

Draw a triangle with its inscribed circle. Join the center of the circle with each vertex of the triangle. Let D, E, and F be the points of tangency of the sides of the triangle.

$AF = AE$; $CD = CE$; $BD = BF$. Why?
$2AF + 2CD + 2BD = 2s$. Why?
$AF + CD + BD = s$. $CD + BD = a$.
Then $AF + a = s$, or $AF = s - a$.

Since AO bisects angle A, and $OF = r$, we have

$$\tan \tfrac{1}{2} A = \frac{r}{s - a}.$$

Interchanging letters, $\tan \tfrac{1}{2} B = \dfrac{r}{s - b}$.

$$\tan \tfrac{1}{2} C = \frac{r}{s - c}.$$

EXAMPLE

Find the smallest angle of a triangle having sides 4, 5, and 7.

The smallest angle is opposite the side 4. Why? Call this angle A. $s = 8$, $s - a = 4$, $s - b = 3$, $s - c = 1$. Then $r = \sqrt{1.5} = 1.225$. Express r to the nearest three-place decimal when using this theorem.

$\tan \tfrac{1}{2} A = \dfrac{1.225}{4} = .3063$. $\tfrac{1}{2} A = 17° \ 1.9'$. Express the half-angle to the nearest tenth of a minute when using this theorem. Then $A = 34° \ 4'$.

EXERCISES

For each of the following problems plan the solution. That is,
(1) Make a scale drawing.
(2) Write what is given and what is required to be found.
(3) Write the formula or formulas that apply in the solution.
(4) Indicate how each formula is to be used in the particular case. The actual computation is to be performed if the instructor so directs.

SOLVING THE GENERAL TRIANGLE

1. Find the slope of the face of a road embankment if the top of a pole 30 feet long reaches 25 feet up the face when the foot of the pole is 12 feet from the foot of the embankment. By the slope of the embankment is meant the acute angle which the face of the embankment makes with the horizontal.

2. Along a shore, radio stations at points C and D lie in a north and south line, with C 32.6 miles north of D. The officers on a ship in distress at point A are listening to radio signals sent out by these stations. By means of a *direction finder* they determine that $\angle DCA = 29°\ 34'$ and $\angle ADC = 117°\ 43'$. Find the distance of the ship from each station.

3. Maple Street and Ash Street intersect at an angle of 65°. A man buys the triangular corner lot for a filling station with 150 feet frontage on Maple Street and 120 feet frontage on Ash Street. What is the area of his lot?

4. From a boat an iceberg is sighted due east which has an elevation of 13°. After the boat has traveled $\frac{3}{8}$ of a mile in the direction N. 18° W., the bearing of the visible base of the iceberg is S. 40° E. Find the height of the iceberg.

5. Two guns are fired at the same instant, and a listener hears the report of the guns 3 seconds and 5 seconds later. The angle at the listener's eye subtended by the distance between the guns is 38° 43'. How far apart are the guns? Assume that sound travels at a rate of 1100 feet per second.

6. At a point A on a paved highway running north and south is a branch highway bearing S. 65° 44' E. From a point C on the first highway 4.5 miles north of the intersection a gravel road runs in a straight line to the branch highway, meeting it at point B 3.8 miles from the intersection. How many miles would a motorist save by taking the gravel road from C to B instead of going through A and then to B?

7. A state highway running due east and west is intersected by a second straight road having a bearing of N. 27° E. At 3:00 o'clock an automobile going east passes the intersection at 50 miles an hour. At 3:10 o'clock an automobile going N. 27° E. on the other road passes the intersection at 45 miles an hour. If these speeds are maintained, how far apart are the automobiles at 3:30 o'clock?

8. A section of the steel framework of a roof of a building is in the form of a triangle with sides 50 feet, 32.5 feet, and 28.3 feet. Find the angles at which the sides must be riveted together.

9. *Finding the distance to the moon.* Let P and P' be the positions of two observers on the same meridian of the earth. Z and Z' are zenith points. The observer at P measures the angle MPZ, and the observer at P' measures the angle $Z'P'M$. The latitudes of points P and P' are known, hence the angle $P'EP$ can be found, E being at the center of the earth. The radius of the earth is known.

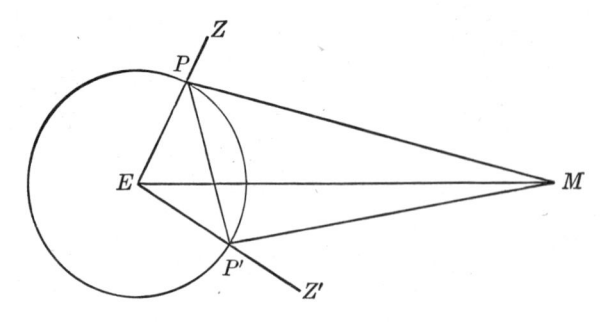

(a) Make a plan for finding the distance PP' and the angles EPP' and $EP'P$.
(b) Show how the angles $P'PM$ and $MP'P$ may be found.
(c) Make a plan for solving the triangle $MP'P$ for MP.
(d) Show how the distance EM can be computed from the triangle EPM.

10. *Finding the diameter of the moon.* By means of an angle-measuring instrument set up at the point P on the earth, the angle CPD, subtended by the diameter of the moon, can be measured.

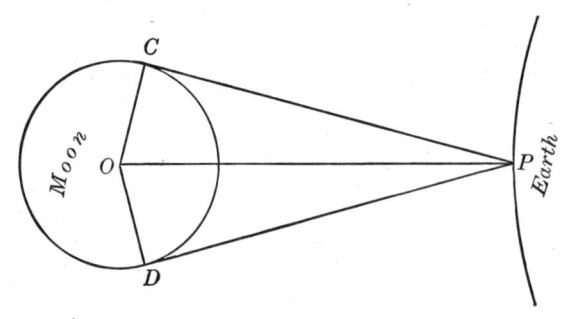

$\angle CPO = \frac{1}{2}$ of $\angle CPD$. Why?
$\angle PCO = 90°$. Why?

$$\sin \angle CPO = \frac{OC}{OP}, \text{ or } OC = OP \sin \angle CPO.$$

If $OP = 239{,}000$ miles and $\angle CPD = 31'\ 5''$, find CD, which is approximately the diameter of the moon (sin $15'\ 32.5'' = .00452$).

11. *An old problem:* A barn 40 feet square is in a pasture. A horse is tied to a rope 100 feet long fastened at one corner (C) of the barn. Find the area over which the horse can graze. *Hint:* The horse can

SOLVING THE GENERAL TRIANGLE

graze over $\frac{3}{4}$ of a circle with radius of 100 feet; over the two triangles EBA and DEA; and over the two sectors FDE and EBG.

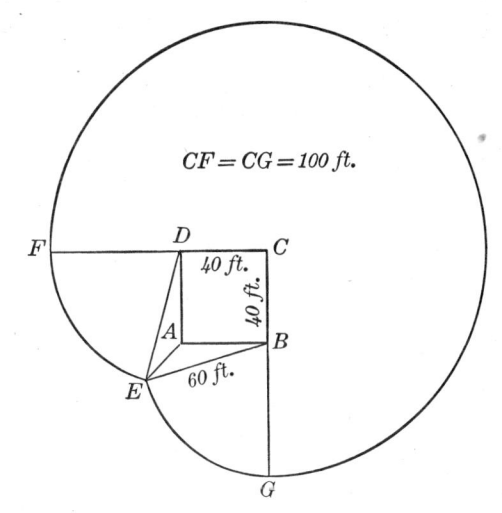

$CF = CG = 100$ ft.

REVIEW QUESTIONS ON CHAPTER IV

1. Explain why the four theorems in Section 23 are needed in the solution of triangles.

2. Prove each of the following: (A is acute) $\sin(180° - A) = \sin A$; $\cos(180° - A) = -\cos A$; $\tan(180° - A) = -\tan A$.

3. Write in words the full statement of the sine theorem; the cosine theorem; the tangent theorem; the tangent half-angle theorem.

4. Give a proof for each theorem of question 3.

5. What parts of a triangle need be given in order that the triangle may be solved (a) by the sine theorem, (b) by the cosine theorem, (c) by the tangent theorem, (d) by the tangent half-angle theorem?

6. Write the formulas for finding the area of a triangle. What parts of a triangle need be given in order to use each formula?

7. Write the formulas for finding the radius of the inscribed circle and the radius of the circumscribed circle.

8. In the triangle ABC, $A = 70°$, $B = 42°$, and $a = 50$. Find b by the use of the sine theorem.

9. In the triangle ABC, $a = 12$, $b = 18$, and $B = 64°$. Find A by the use of the sine theorem.

10. In the triangle ABC, $a = 40$, $b = 50$, and $C = 35°$. Find c.

11. In the triangle ABC, $a = 9$, $b = 14$, and $c = 20$. Find B.

12. In the triangle ABC, $a = 18$, $c = 40$, and $B = 50° 20'$. Use the tangent theorem to find A and C.

13. In the triangle ABC, $a = 24$, $b = 20$, and $c = 16$. Use the tangent half-angle theorem to find A, B, and C.

14. Find r and R for the following data: (a) $a = 30$, $b = 18$, $C = 42°$. (b) $a = 12$, $A = 35°$, $B = 22°$. (c) $a = 8$, $b = 12$, $c = 15$.

The Twofold Nature of Trigonometry

THE name, trigonometry, and most of the discussion in the preceding chapters associate the subject with practical problems in the solution of the triangle. This is only one part of trigonometry. The other is concerned with a study of the relationships between the functions themselves. Most of the material in Chapters V, VI, and IX is of this nature.

This latter phase of the subject is called *trigonometric analysis*, and is almost entirely lacking in trigonometries before 1600. It was made possible by the invention of an adequate algebraic symbolism with the resulting increased attention to the study of algebra.

As analytic geometry, the calculus, and other mathematical subjects came into existence, they found much use for the trigonometric relationships already developed. Then the power inherent in these new subjects made it possible to discover valuable new ideas involving trigonometric functions.

The student who continues his study of mathematics beyond trigonometry will see the use of trigonometric analysis in his work; and all should learn to appreciate the theoretical aspects and to enjoy discovering some of the many remarkable combinations of which the trigonometric functions are capable.

CHAPTER

V

Fundamental Trigonometric Relations

IN the preceding chapters trigonometry has been used to solve triangles. Now interesting properties about the functions themselves, which are very useful in advanced mathematics, are to be presented.

31. Reciprocal functions

From the definition of the trigonometric functions given in Chapter II it is easily observed that

$$\sin A = \frac{1}{\csc A}.$$

$$\cos A = \frac{1}{\sec A}.$$

$$\tan A = \frac{1}{\cot A}.$$

32. Sine and cosine

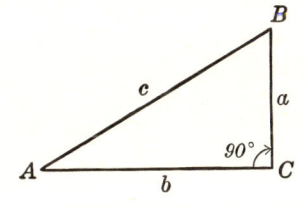

In the right triangle ACB

$$a^2 + b^2 = c^2.$$

77

Dividing each member of this equation by c^2 gives

$$\frac{a^2}{c^2} + \frac{b^2}{c^2} = 1 \text{ or}$$

$$\left(\frac{a}{c}\right)^2 + \left(\frac{b}{c}\right)^2 = 1.$$

$$\sin^2 A + \cos^2 A = 1.$$

33. Tangent and secant

Divide each member of the equation $a^2 + b^2 = c^2$ by b^2.

$$\left(\frac{a}{b}\right)^2 + 1 = \left(\frac{c}{b}\right)^2.$$

Then
$$1 + \tan^2 A = \sec^2 A.$$

34. Cotangent and cosecant

Divide each member of the equation $a^2 + b^2 = c^2$ by a^2.

$$1 + \left(\frac{b}{a}\right)^2 = \left(\frac{c}{a}\right)^2.$$

Then
$$1 + \cot^2 A = \csc^2 A.$$

35. Sine, cosine, and tangent

$$\frac{a}{c} = \sin A; \quad \frac{b}{c} = \cos A.$$

Dividing,
$$\frac{a}{c} \div \frac{b}{c} = \frac{a}{b} = \frac{\sin A}{\cos A}.$$

But
$$\frac{a}{b} = \tan A.$$

Then
$$\tan A = \frac{\sin A}{\cos A}.$$

In a like manner it may be shown that

$$\cot A = \frac{\cos A}{\sin A}.$$

36. Verifying identities

The fundamental relations between the functions should be memorized. Many times it is necessary to change an expression so that only one function appears, or it is required to verify certain identities. The following examples should be carefully

FUNDAMENTAL TRIGONOMETRIC RELATIONS

studied, in order to learn the procedure to be used in verifying identities.

EXAMPLES

1. Show that $(\sin A - \cos A)^2 = 1 - 2 \sin A \cos A$.
$$\sin^2 A - 2 \sin A \cos A + \cos^2 A = 1 - 2 \sin A \cos A.$$
Since $\sin^2 A + \cos^2 A = 1$,
$$1 - 2 \sin A \cos A = 1 - 2 \sin A \cos A.$$

2. Show that $\dfrac{1}{\sin A (\tan A + \cot A)} = \cos A$.

Rewriting the left member using sines and cosines, we have
$$\frac{1}{\sin A \left[\dfrac{\sin A}{\cos A} + \dfrac{\cos A}{\sin A}\right]} = \cos A,$$
since $\tan A = \dfrac{\sin A}{\cos A}$, and $\cot A = \dfrac{\cos A}{\sin A}$.

$$\frac{1}{\sin A \left[\dfrac{\sin^2 A + \cos^2 A}{\cos A \sin A}\right]} = \cos A.$$

$$\frac{1}{\sin A \left[\dfrac{1}{\cos A \sin A}\right]} = \cos A, \text{ since } \sin^2 A + \cos^2 A = 1.$$

$$\frac{1}{\left[\dfrac{1}{\cos A}\right]} = \cos A.$$

$$\cos A = \cos A.$$

3. Show that $\cos^4 A - \sin^4 A = 2 \cos^2 A - 1$.
$$(\cos^2 A + \sin^2 A)(\cos^2 A - \sin^2 A) = 2 \cos^2 A - 1.$$
Since $\sin^2 A + \cos^2 A = 1$,
$$\cos^2 A - \sin^2 A = 2 \cos^2 A - 1.$$
$\sin^2 A = 1 - \cos^2 A$. Substitute this expression for $\sin^2 A$ in the above left member. Then
$$\cos^2 A - (1 - \cos^2 A) = 2 \cos^2 A - 1.$$
$$2 \cos^2 A - 1 = 2 \cos^2 A - 1.$$

37. Expressing all functions in terms of one function

The use of a scale triangle with a function represented by a side will be very helpful in expressing all functions in terms of that function.

Examples

1. Express all the functions of A in terms of $\sin A$.

Draw a scale right triangle having a hypotenuse of 1 unit. It is easily seen that the side opposite angle A represents $\sin A$, since $\sin A = \dfrac{\sin A}{1}$.

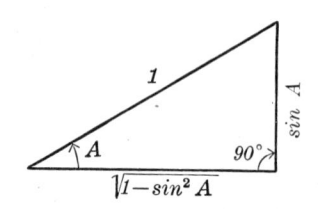

$$\cos A = \sqrt{1 - \sin^2 A}; \quad \sec A = \frac{1}{\sqrt{1 - \sin^2 A}};$$

$$\tan A = \frac{\sin A}{\sqrt{1 - \sin^2 A}}; \quad \cot A = \frac{\sqrt{1 - \sin^2 A}}{\sin A}; \quad \csc A = \frac{1}{\sin A}.$$

2. Express all functions of A in terms of $\tan A$.

Draw a scale right triangle having a base of 1 unit. Then the side opposite angle A represents $\tan A$, since $\tan A = \dfrac{\tan A}{1}$.

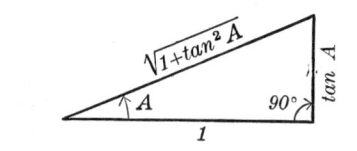

$$\sin A = \frac{\tan A}{\sqrt{1 + \tan^2 A}}; \quad \cos A = \frac{1}{\sqrt{1 + \tan^2 A}};$$

$$\sec A = \sqrt{1 + \tan^2 A}; \quad \csc A = \frac{\sqrt{1 + \tan^2 A}}{\tan A}; \quad \cot A = \frac{1}{\tan A}.$$

3. Express $\tan A + \cot A$ in terms of sines and cosines.

$$\tan A + \cot A = \frac{\sin A}{\cos A} + \frac{\cos A}{\sin A} = \frac{\sin^2 A + \cos^2 A}{\sin A \cos A} = \frac{1}{\sin A \cos A}.$$

EXERCISES

1. Express $\cos A$ in terms of the other functions.
2. Express all the functions in terms of $\cos A$.
3. Express all the functions in terms of $\sec A$.

Verify the following identities. In the verification of identities it is urged that the left member be changed to read the same as the right member, or the reverse. Do not use the algebraic substitution to prove any identity; that is, do not substitute $\frac{a}{c}$ for sin A, etc.

4. $(1 - \sec^2 A)(1 - \csc^2 A) = 1$.
5. $\tan^2 A (\csc^2 A - 1) = 1$.
6. $\sin^2 A (1 + \cot^2 A) = 1$.
7. $\cot^2 A - \cos^2 A = \cot^2 A \cos^2 A$.
8. $\cos A \sin A (\cot A + \tan A) = 1$.
9. $\dfrac{1 + \cot^2 A}{1 + \tan^2 A} = \cot^2 A$.
10. $(\tan A - \cot A) \sin A \cos A = \sin^2 A - \cos^2 A$.
11. $\sqrt{\sec^2 A + \csc^2 A} = \tan A + \cot A$.
12. $\sec^4 A - \tan^4 A = \sec^2 A + \tan^2 A$.
13. $1 - \tan^4 A = 2 \sec^2 A - \sec^4 A$.
14. $\dfrac{1 + \cos A}{1 - \cos A} = (\csc A + \cot A)^2$.
15. $(\sin A + \cos A)^2 + (\sin A - \cos A)^2 = 2$.
16. $\dfrac{\cot A \cos A}{\cot A + \cos A} = \dfrac{\cot A - \cos A}{\cot A \cos A}$.
17. $\cot A \cos A + \sin A = \csc A$.
18. $\sin^3 A + \cos^3 A = (\sin A + \cos A)(1 - \sin A \cos A)$.
19. $\sin^6 A + \cos^6 A = 1 - 3 \sin^2 A \cos^2 A$.

38. Solving trigonometric equations

In a trigonometric equation the unknown is a *function of an angle*. The angle which reduces the equation to an identity is a *solution*. If several different functions of the angle are involved in the equation, the first step in the solution is to express all functions in terms of a single function.

Examples

1. Find the acute angle which is a solution of the equation $\sec A \cot A = \frac{4}{3}$.

The left member of the equation may be written

$$\frac{1}{\cos A} \times \frac{\cos A}{\sin A} = \frac{1}{\sin A}.$$

Then $\dfrac{1}{\sin A} = \frac{4}{3}$, or $\sin A = \frac{3}{4} = .7500$. $A = 48° 36'$.

2. Solve the equation $2 \sin A = 2 - \cos A$.

The equation reduces to $2\sqrt{1 - \cos^2 A} = 2 - \cos A$. Squaring each member of this equation gives

$$4 - 4 \cos^2 A = 4 - 4 \cos A + \cos^2 A.$$

Rearranging, $\cos A (5 \cos A - 4) = 0$.
Then $\cos A = 0$ or $\cos A = \frac{4}{5}$.
$A = 90°$ or $36° 52'$.

3. Solve the equation $2 \tan^2 A - 5 \tan A + 3 = 0$.
Factoring, $(\tan A - 1)(2 \tan A - 3) = 0$.
Then $\tan A - 1 = 0$, or $2 \tan A - 3 = 0$.
$\tan A = 1$, or $\tan A = \frac{3}{2} = 1.5$.
$A = 45°$ or $56° 19'$.

EXERCISES

Find the angles to the nearest minute from 0° to 90° inclusive that are solutions of the equations. When square roots are to be found, use only the positive square root.

1. $2 \cos A = \sec A$.
2. $4 \sin A = 3 \csc A$.
3. $4 \cos A - 3 \sec A = 0$.
4. $\sqrt{2} \sin A - \tan A = 0$.
5. $\sin A - \cos A = 0$.
6. $3 \tan A - 4 \sin A = 0$.
7. $8 \cos^2 A = 10 \cos A - 3$.
8. $6 \sin^2 A - 5 \sin A + 1 = 0$.
9. $\tan A + 3 \cot A - 4 = 0$.
10. $\sec^2 A + \cos^2 A - 7 = 0$.
11. $\sin A + \cos A = \sec A$.
12. $\cos A = 2 (1 - \sin A)$.
13. $\sin A + \sqrt{3} \cos A = 2$.
14. $\tan^2 A - 1 = 2 (\sin^2 A - \cos^2 A)$.
15. $2 \cos A + \sec A = 3$.

In the exercises and applications thus far studied we have used only the functions of a single angle. There are many kinds of exercises in which it is convenient to consider the functions of two or more angles. The fundamental relations which will be developed in the next sections have many important uses and applications.

FUNDAMENTAL TRIGONOMETRIC RELATIONS

39. Sine of the sum of two angles

The sine of the sum of two angles is equal to the sine of the first angle times the cosine of the second angle, plus the cosine of the first angle times the sine of the second angle.

$$\sin (A + B) = \sin A \cos B + \cos A \sin B.$$

Proof: In the figures, $\angle XOY = A$ and $\angle YOZ = B$. Then $\angle XOZ = (A + B)$.

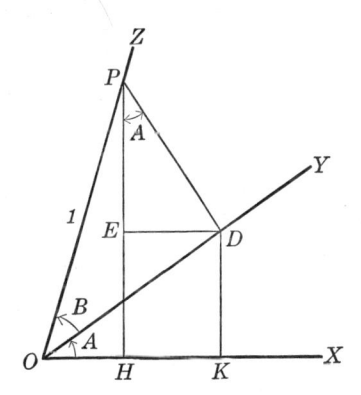

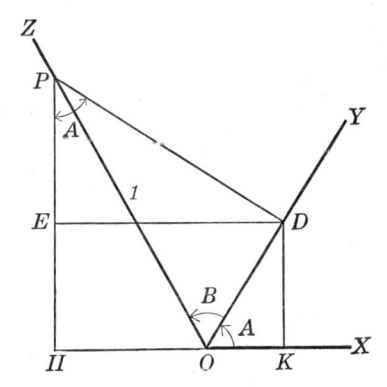

On OZ mark off a distance $OP = 1$. Draw PH perpendicular to OX and PD perpendicular to OY. KD is perpendicular to OX, and ED is perpendicular to HP. $\angle EPD = A$. Why?

$\sin (A + B) = HP = HE + EP = KD + EP.$
In the triangle OKD, $KD = OD \sin A$. Why?
In the triangle DEP, $EP = DP \cos A$. Why?
$\qquad \sin (A + B) = OD \sin A + DP \cos A.$
In the triangle ODP, $OD = \cos B$, and $DP = \sin B$.
$\qquad \sin (A + B) = \sin A \cos B + \cos A \sin B.$

Example

$\sin (30° + 45°) = \sin 75° = \sin 30° \cos 45° + \cos 30° \sin 45°.$

$$\sin 75° = \frac{1}{2} \times \frac{1}{\sqrt{2}} + \frac{\sqrt{3}}{2} \times \frac{1}{\sqrt{2}} = \frac{1}{2\sqrt{2}} + \frac{\sqrt{3}}{2\sqrt{2}} = \frac{1 + \sqrt{3}}{2\sqrt{2}}.$$

$$\sin 75° = \frac{1 + \sqrt{3}}{2\sqrt{2}} = \frac{1 + \sqrt{3}}{2\sqrt{2}} \times \frac{\sqrt{2}}{\sqrt{2}} = \frac{\sqrt{2} + \sqrt{6}}{4} = .9659.$$

Find $\sin 75°$ in the tables. Is the above answer correct?

40. Cosine of the sum of two angles

The cosine of the sum of two angles is equal to the cosine of the first angle times the cosine of the second angle, minus the sine of the first angle times the sine of the second angle.

$$\cos (A + B) = \cos A \cos B - \sin A \sin B.$$

Proof: See the figure on page 83.
$\cos (A + B) = OH = OK - HK = OK - ED.$
In the second figure $HO = ED - OK;\ -HO = OK - ED;$ $OH = OK - ED.$
In the triangle $OKD,\ OK = OD \cos A.$
In the triangle $DEP,\ ED = DP \sin A.$
$\cos (A + B) = OD \cos A - DP \sin A = \cos A \cos B - \sin A \sin B.$

Example

$\cos (30° + 45°) = \cos 75° = \cos 30° \cos 45° - \sin 30° \sin 45°.$

$$\cos 75° = \frac{\sqrt{3}}{2} \times \frac{1}{\sqrt{2}} - \frac{1}{2} \times \frac{1}{\sqrt{2}}.$$

$$\cos 75° = \frac{\sqrt{3} - 1}{2\sqrt{2}} = \frac{\sqrt{6} - \sqrt{2}}{4} = .2588.$$

Find $\cos 75°$ in the tables. Is the above answer correct?

Caution: The sine of the sum of two angles is *not equal* to the sum of the sines of the angles. The cosine of the sum of two angles is *not equal* to the sum of the cosines of the angles. See figures on page 83.

EXERCISES

1. Since $\sin 60° = \sin (30° + 30°)$, show that $\sin 60° = \frac{\sqrt{3}}{2}.$

2. Show similarly that $\cos 60° = \frac{1}{2}.$

3. Since $120° = 60° + 60°$, show that $\sin 120° = \frac{\sqrt{3}}{2} = \sin 60°.$

4. Show similarly that $\cos 120° = -\frac{1}{2} = -\cos 60°.$

5. Since $150° = 120° + 30°$, show that $\sin 150° = \frac{1}{2} = \sin 30°.$

6. Show that $\cos 150° = -\frac{\sqrt{3}}{2} = -\cos 30°.$

7. Does $\sin 15° = \sin 8° + \sin 7°$?
Does $\cos 40° = \cos 30° + \cos 10°$?

FUNDAMENTAL TRIGONOMETRIC RELATIONS

Example

Given $\sin A = \frac{3}{5}$ and $\sin B = \frac{5}{13}$. Find $\sin(A+B)$ and $\cos(A+B)$. Then find the angle $(A+B)$.

First construct the scale triangle for each angle.

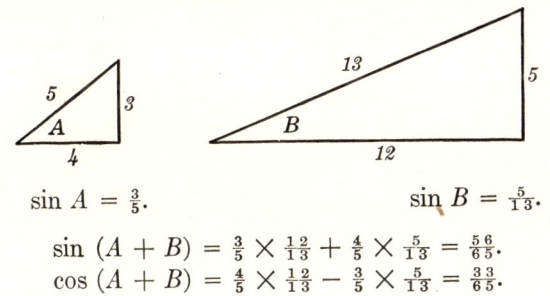

$\sin A = \frac{3}{5}$. $\qquad \sin B = \frac{5}{13}$.

$\sin(A+B) = \frac{3}{5} \times \frac{12}{13} + \frac{4}{5} \times \frac{5}{13} = \frac{56}{65}$.
$\cos(A+B) = \frac{4}{5} \times \frac{12}{13} - \frac{3}{5} \times \frac{5}{13} = \frac{33}{65}$.

Since the sine and the cosine of the sum of A and B are positive, $(A+B)$ is an acute angle.

$\sin(A+B) = \frac{56}{65} = .8615$.
$(A+B) = 59° \, 29'$.

EXERCISES

1. Given $\sin A = \frac{3}{5}$ and $\cos B = \frac{15}{17}$. Show that $\sin(A+B) = \frac{77}{85}$. Find $(A+B)$ in degrees. $\cos(A+B) = ?$

2. Given $\cos A = \frac{\sqrt{3}}{2}$ and $\cos B = \frac{1}{3}$. Show that $\sin(A+B) = \frac{1 + 2\sqrt{6}}{6}$. Also show that $\cos(A+B) = \frac{\sqrt{3} - 2\sqrt{2}}{6}$. Is $(A+B)$ acute or obtuse? Why?

3. Given $\tan A = \frac{1}{2}$ and $\sin B = \frac{1}{\sqrt{10}}$. Show that $(A+B) = 45°$.

4. Given $\sin A = \frac{3}{5}$ and $\cos B = -\frac{1}{2}$, (B is obtuse). Is $(A+B)$ acute or obtuse? Why?

41. Tangent of the sum of two angles

The tangent of the sum of two angles is equal to a fraction whose numerator is the sum of the tangents of the two angles and whose denominator is 1 minus the product of the tangents.

$$\tan(A+B) = \frac{\tan A + \tan B}{1 - \tan A \tan B}.$$

Proof: We have learned that the tangent of an angle is equal to the sine of the angle divided by the cosine of the angle. We have also developed expressions for sin $(A + B)$ and cos $(A + B)$. Then

$$\tan (A + B) = \frac{\sin (A + B)}{\cos (A + B)} = \frac{\sin A \cos B + \cos A \sin B}{\cos A \cos B - \sin A \sin B}.$$

Divide each term of the numerator and denominator of the fraction by cos A cos B.

$$\tan (A + B) = \frac{\dfrac{\sin A}{\cos A} + \dfrac{\sin B}{\cos B}}{1 - \dfrac{\sin A \sin B}{\cos A \cos B}} = \frac{\tan A + \tan B}{1 - \tan A \tan B}.$$

EXAMPLE

$$\tan (30° + 45°) = \tan 75° = \frac{\dfrac{1}{\sqrt{3}} + 1}{1 - \dfrac{1}{\sqrt{3}}} = \frac{\sqrt{3} + 1}{\sqrt{3} - 1} = 3.7321.$$

Find tan 75° in the tables. Is the above answer correct?

Caution: The tangent of the sum of two angles is *not equal* to the sum of the tangents of the angles.

EXERCISES

1. Since $30° + 30° = 60°$, show that $\tan 60° = \sqrt{3}$.
2. Using $60° + 60° = 120°$, show that $\tan 120° = -\sqrt{3} = -\tan 60°$.
3. Using $120° + 30° = 150°$, show that $\tan 150° = -\dfrac{1}{\sqrt{3}} = -\tan 30°$.
4. Given $\tan A = \frac{1}{2}$ and $\tan B = \frac{1}{3}$, show that $(A + B) = 45°$.
5. Given $\tan A = \frac{1}{3}$ and $\tan B = 1$, show that $\tan (A + B) = 2$.
6. Given $\tan A = \frac{3}{2}$ and $\tan B = \frac{3}{4}$, show that $\tan (A + B) = -18$. Is $(A + B)$ acute or obtuse? Why?
7. Given $\tan A = \frac{5}{6}$ and $\tan B = \frac{1}{11}$. Show that $(A + B) = 45°$.
8. Give a geometrical proof for the expression of the tangent of the sum of two angles. See the figure on page 83.

42. Sine of the difference of two angles

The sine of the difference of two angles is equal to the sine of the first angle times the cosine of the second angle, minus the cosine of the first angle times the sine of the second angle.

$$\sin (A - B) = \sin A \cos B - \cos A \sin B.$$

Proof: The proof is given only for A and B acute. Later it

SOLVING THE GENERAL TRIANGLE

Then
$$\sin A = \frac{h}{c};$$

Hence
$$\frac{a}{2R} = \frac{h}{c},$$

and
$$R = \frac{ac}{2h}. \qquad (2)$$

We know that $\frac{1}{2} bh = K$.

Substituting the value of $h = \frac{2K}{b}$ in (2) gives

$$R = \frac{abc}{4K}.$$

EXAMPLE

Find the radius of the circumscribed circle for the triangle when $a = 8$, $b = 12$, and $c = 14$.

$K = \sqrt{s(s-a)(s-b)(s-c)}$. $s = 17$, $s - a = 9$, $s - b = 5$, and $s - c = 3$.

$$R = \frac{8 \times 12 \times 14}{4\sqrt{17 \times 9 \times 5 \times 3}} = 7.01.$$

EXERCISES

1. Using the relation (1) on page 70, show how the formula for the *sine theorem* may be developed, that is,

$$2R = \frac{a}{\sin A} = \frac{b}{\sin B} = \frac{c}{\sin C}.$$

2. Find the radii of the inscribed and circumscribed circles for the triangles.

    (a) $a = 8$, $b = 10$, $c = 12$.
    (b) $a = 8$, $b = 15$, $c = 17$.

3. Find R when
    (a) $a = 18$, $A = 50°$.
    (b) $a = 40$, $A = 120°$.
    (c) $b = 48$, $B = 30°$.
    (d) $c = 100$, $C = 42°$.

30. Tangent half-angle theorem

In any triangle the tangent of half of any angle is equal to the quotient of the radius of the inscribed circle divided by the difference between the semi-perimeter of the triangle and the side opposite the specified angle.

Given the three sides of a triangle, find the angles.

We can find the angles by using the *cosine theorem*, but often it is more convenient to use the *tangent half-angle theorem*. In general the tangent half-angle theorem gives more accurate results.

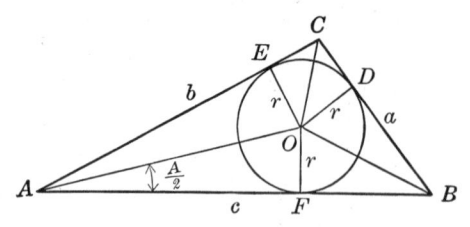

Draw a triangle with its inscribed circle. Join the center of the circle with each vertex of the triangle. Let D, E, and F be the points of tangency of the sides of the triangle.

$AF = AE$; $CD = CE$; $BD = BF$. Why?
$2AF + 2CD + 2BD = 2s$. Why?
$AF + CD + BD = s$. $CD + BD = a$.
  Then $AF + a = s$, or $AF = s - a$.

Since AO bisects angle A, and $OF = r$, we have

$$\tan \tfrac{1}{2} A = \frac{r}{s-a}.$$

Interchanging letters, $\tan \tfrac{1}{2} B = \dfrac{r}{s-b}.$

$$\tan \tfrac{1}{2} C = \frac{r}{s-c}.$$

EXAMPLE

Find the smallest angle of a triangle having sides 4, 5, and 7.

The smallest angle is opposite the side 4. Why? Call this angle A. $s = 8$, $s - a = 4$, $s - b = 3$, $s - c = 1$. Then $r = \sqrt{1.5} = 1.225$. Express r to the nearest three-place decimal when using this theorem.

$\tan \tfrac{1}{2} A = \dfrac{1.225}{4} = .3063.$ $\tfrac{1}{2} A = 17° 1.9'$. Express the half-angle to the nearest tenth of a minute when using this theorem. Then $A = 34° 4'$.

EXERCISES

For each of the following problems plan the solution. That is,
(1) *Make a scale drawing.*
(2) *Write what is given and what is required to be found.*
(3) *Write the formula or formulas that apply in the solution.*
(4) *Indicate how each formula is to be used in the particular case.*
The actual computation is to be performed if the instructor so directs.

SOLVING THE GENERAL TRIANGLE

1. Find the slope of the face of a road embankment if the top of a pole 30 feet long reaches 25 feet up the face when the foot of the pole is 12 feet from the foot of the embankment. By the slope of the embankment is meant the acute angle which the face of the embankment makes with the horizontal.

2. Along a shore, radio stations at points C and D lie in a north and south line, with C 32.6 miles north of D. The officers on a ship in distress at point A are listening to radio signals sent out by these stations. By means of a *direction finder* they determine that $\angle DCA = 29° 34'$ and $\angle ADC = 117° 43'$. Find the distance of the ship from each station.

3. Maple Street and Ash Street intersect at an angle of 65°. A man buys the triangular corner lot for a filling station with 150 feet frontage on Maple Street and 120 feet frontage on Ash Street. What is the area of his lot?

4. From a boat an iceberg is sighted due east which has an elevation of 13°. After the boat has traveled $\frac{3}{8}$ of a mile in the direction N. 18° W., the bearing of the visible base of the iceberg is S. 40° E. Find the height of the iceberg.

5. Two guns are fired at the same instant, and a listener hears the report of the guns 3 seconds and 5 seconds later. The angle at the listener's eye subtended by the distance between the guns is 38° 43'. How far apart are the guns? Assume that sound travels at a rate of 1100 feet per second.

6. At a point A on a paved highway running north and south is a branch highway bearing S. 65° 44' E. From a point C on the first highway 4.5 miles north of the intersection a gravel road runs in a straight line to the branch highway, meeting it at point B 3.8 miles from the intersection. How many miles would a motorist save by taking the gravel road from C to B instead of going through A and then to B?

7. A state highway running due east and west is intersected by a second straight road having a bearing of N. 27° E. At 3:00 o'clock an automobile going east passes the intersection at 50 miles an hour. At 3:10 o'clock an automobile going N. 27° E. on the other road passes the intersection at 45 miles an hour. If these speeds are maintained, how far apart are the automobiles at 3:30 o'clock?

8. A section of the steel framework of a roof of a building is in the form of a triangle with sides 50 feet, 32.5 feet, and 28.3 feet. Find the angles at which the sides must be riveted together.

9. *Finding the distance to the moon.* Let P and P' be the positions of two observers on the same meridian of the earth. Z and Z' are zenith points. The observer at P measures the angle MPZ, and the observer at P' measures the angle $Z'P'M$. The latitudes of points P and P' are known, hence the angle $P'EP$ can be found, E being at the center of the earth. The radius of the earth is known.

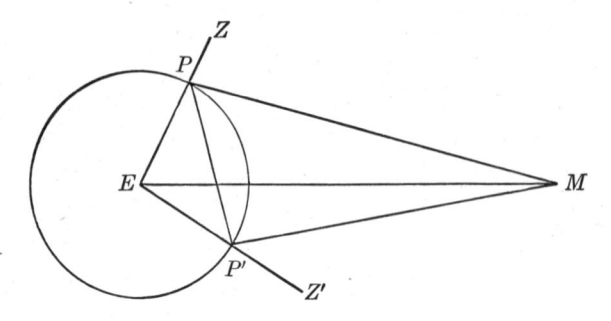

(a) Make a plan for finding the distance PP' and the angles EPP' and $EP'P$.
(b) Show how the angles $P'PM$ and $MP'P$ may be found.
(c) Make a plan for solving the triangle $MP'P$ for MP.
(d) Show how the distance EM can be computed from the triangle EPM.

10. *Finding the diameter of the moon.* By means of an angle-measuring instrument set up at the point P on the earth, the angle CPD, subtended by the diameter of the moon, can be measured.

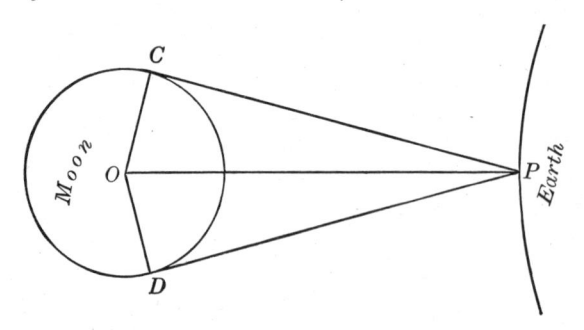

$\angle CPO = \frac{1}{2}$ of $\angle CPD$. Why?
$\angle PCO = 90°$. Why?

$$\sin \angle CPO = \frac{OC}{OP}, \text{ or } OC = OP \sin \angle CPO.$$

If $OP = 239{,}000$ miles and $\angle CPD = 31'\ 5''$, find CD, which is approximately the diameter of the moon ($\sin 15'\ 32.5'' = .00452$).

11. *An old problem:* A barn 40 feet square is in a pasture. A horse is tied to a rope 100 feet long fastened at one corner (C) of the barn. Find the area over which the horse can graze. *Hint:* The horse can

SOLVING THE GENERAL TRIANGLE

graze over $\frac{3}{4}$ of a circle with radius of 100 feet; over the two triangles EBA and DEA; and over the two sectors FDE and EBG.

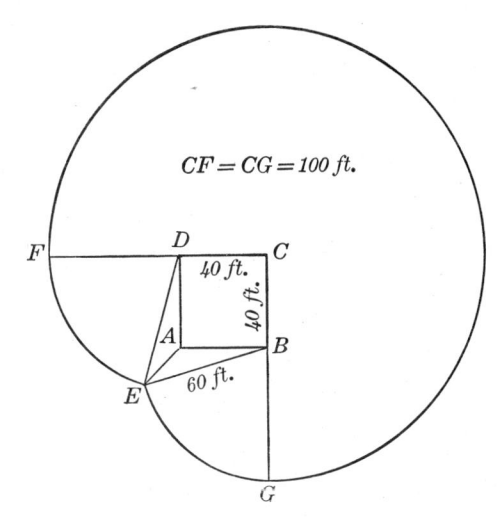

$CF = CG = 100$ ft.

40 ft. (CD)
40 ft. (CB)
60 ft. (EB)

REVIEW QUESTIONS ON CHAPTER IV

1. Explain why the four theorems in Section 23 are needed in the solution of triangles.

2. Prove each of the following: (A is acute) $\sin(180° - A) = \sin A$; $\cos(180° - A) = -\cos A$; $\tan(180° - A) = -\tan A$.

3. Write in words the full statement of the sine theorem; the cosine theorem; the tangent theorem; the tangent half-angle theorem.

4. Give a proof for each theorem of question 3.

5. What parts of a triangle need be given in order that the triangle may be solved (a) by the sine theorem, (b) by the cosine theorem, (c) by the tangent theorem, (d) by the tangent half-angle theorem?

6. Write the formulas for finding the area of a triangle. What parts of a triangle need be given in order to use each formula?

7. Write the formulas for finding the radius of the inscribed circle and the radius of the circumscribed circle.

8. In the triangle ABC, $A = 70°$, $B = 42°$, and $a = 50$. Find b by the use of the sine theorem.

9. In the triangle ABC, $a = 12$, $b = 18$, and $B = 64°$. Find A by the use of the sine theorem.

10. In the triangle ABC, $a = 40$, $b = 50$, and $C = 35°$. Find c.

11. In the triangle ABC, $a = 9$, $b = 14$, and $c = 20$. Find B.

12. In the triangle ABC, $a = 18$, $c = 40$, and $B = 50° 20'$. Use the tangent theorem to find A and C.

13. In the triangle ABC, $a = 24$, $b = 20$, and $c = 10$. Use the tangent half-angle theorem to find A, B, and C.

14. Find r and R for the following data: (a) $a = 30$, $b = 18$, $C = 42°$. (b) $a = 12$, $A = 35°$, $B = 22°$. (c) $a = 8$, $b = 12$, $c = 15$.

The Twofold Nature of Trigonometry

THE name, trigonometry, and most of the discussion in the preceding chapters associate the subject with practical problems in the solution of the triangle. This is only one part of trigonometry. The other is concerned with a study of the relationships between the functions themselves. Most of the material in Chapters V, VI, and IX is of this nature.

This latter phase of the subject is called *trigonometric analysis*, and is almost entirely lacking in trigonometries before 1600. It was made possible by the invention of an adequate algebraic symbolism with the resulting increased attention to the study of algebra.

As analytic geometry, the calculus, and other mathematical subjects came into existence, they found much use for the trigonometric relationships already developed. Then the power inherent in these new subjects made it possible to discover valuable new ideas involving trigonometric functions.

The student who continues his study of mathematics beyond trigonometry will see the use of trigonometric analysis in his work; and all should learn to appreciate the theoretical aspects and to enjoy discovering some of the many remarkable combinations of which the trigonometric functions are capable.

CHAPTER

V

Fundamental Trigonometric Relations

IN the preceding chapters trigonometry has been used to solve triangles. Now interesting properties about the functions themselves, which are very useful in advanced mathematics, are to be presented.

31. Reciprocal functions

From the definition of the trigonometric functions given in Chapter II it is easily observed that

$$\sin A = \frac{1}{\csc A}.$$

$$\cos A = \frac{1}{\sec A}.$$

$$\tan A = \frac{1}{\cot A}.$$

32. Sine and cosine

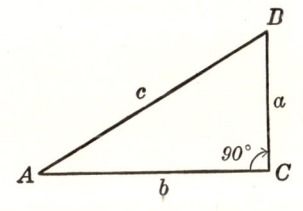

In the right triangle ACB

$$a^2 + b^2 = c^2.$$

Dividing each member of this equation by c^2 gives

$$\frac{a^2}{c^2} + \frac{b^2}{c^2} = 1 \text{ or}$$

$$\left(\frac{a}{c}\right)^2 + \left(\frac{b}{c}\right)^2 = 1.$$

$$\sin^2 A + \cos^2 A = 1.$$

33. Tangent and secant

Divide each member of the equation $a^2 + b^2 = c^2$ by b^2.

$$\left(\frac{a}{b}\right)^2 + 1 = \left(\frac{c}{b}\right)^2.$$

Then
$$1 + \tan^2 A = \sec^2 A.$$

34. Cotangent and cosecant

Divide each member of the equation $a^2 + b^2 = c^2$ by a^2.

$$1 + \left(\frac{b}{a}\right)^2 = \left(\frac{c}{a}\right)^2.$$

Then
$$1 + \cot^2 A = \csc^2 A.$$

35. Sine, cosine, and tangent

$$\frac{a}{c} = \sin A; \frac{b}{c} = \cos A.$$

Dividing,
$$\frac{a}{c} \div \frac{b}{c} = \frac{a}{b} = \frac{\sin A}{\cos A}.$$

But
$$\frac{a}{b} = \tan A.$$

Then
$$\tan A = \frac{\sin A}{\cos A}.$$

In a like manner it may be shown that

$$\cot A = \frac{\cos A}{\sin A}.$$

36. Verifying identities

The fundamental relations between the functions should be memorized. Many times it is necessary to change an expression so that only one function appears, or it is required to verify certain identities. The following examples should be carefully

FUNDAMENTAL TRIGONOMETRIC RELATIONS

studied, in order to learn the procedure to be used in verifying identities.

EXAMPLES

1. Show that $(\sin A - \cos A)^2 = 1 - 2 \sin A \cos A$.
$\sin^2 A - 2 \sin A \cos A + \cos^2 A = 1 - 2 \sin A \cos A$.
Since $\sin^2 A + \cos^2 A = 1$,
$1 - 2 \sin A \cos A = 1 - 2 \sin A \cos A$.

2. Show that $\dfrac{1}{\sin A (\tan A + \cot A)} = \cos A$.

Rewriting the left member using sines and cosines, we have

$$\frac{1}{\sin A \left[\dfrac{\sin A}{\cos A} + \dfrac{\cos A}{\sin A}\right]} = \cos A,$$

since $\tan A = \dfrac{\sin A}{\cos A}$, and $\cot A = \dfrac{\cos A}{\sin A}$.

$$\frac{1}{\sin A \left[\dfrac{\sin^2 A + \cos^2 A}{\cos A \sin A}\right]} = \cos A.$$

$$\frac{1}{\sin A \left[\dfrac{1}{\cos A \sin A}\right]} = \cos A, \text{ since } \sin^2 A + \cos^2 A = 1.$$

$$\frac{1}{\left[\dfrac{1}{\cos A}\right]} = \cos A.$$

$\cos A = \cos A$.

3. Show that $\cos^4 A - \sin^4 A = 2 \cos^2 A - 1$.
$(\cos^2 A + \sin^2 A)(\cos^2 A - \sin^2 A) = 2 \cos^2 A - 1$.
Since $\sin^2 A + \cos^2 A = 1$,
$\cos^2 A - \sin^2 A = 2 \cos^2 A - 1$.
$\sin^2 A = 1 - \cos^2 A$. Substitute this expression for $\sin^2 A$ in the above left member. Then
$\cos^2 A - (1 - \cos^2 A) = 2 \cos^2 A - 1$.
$2 \cos^2 A - 1 = 2 \cos^2 A - 1$.

37. Expressing all functions in terms of one function

The use of a scale triangle with a function represented by a side will be very helpful in expressing all functions in terms of that function.

EXAMPLES

1. Express all the functions of A in terms of $\sin A$.

Draw a scale right triangle having a hypotenuse of 1 unit. It is easily seen that the side opposite angle A represents $\sin A$, since $\sin A = \dfrac{\sin A}{1}$.

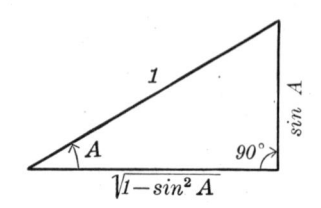

$$\cos A = \sqrt{1 - \sin^2 A}; \sec A = \frac{1}{\sqrt{1 - \sin^2 A}};$$

$$\tan A = \frac{\sin A}{\sqrt{1 - \sin^2 A}}; \cot A = \frac{\sqrt{1 - \sin^2 A}}{\sin A}; \csc A = \frac{1}{\sin A}.$$

2. Express all functions of A in terms of $\tan A$.

Draw a scale right triangle having a base of 1 unit. Then the side opposite angle A represents $\tan A$, since $\tan A = \dfrac{\tan A}{1}$.

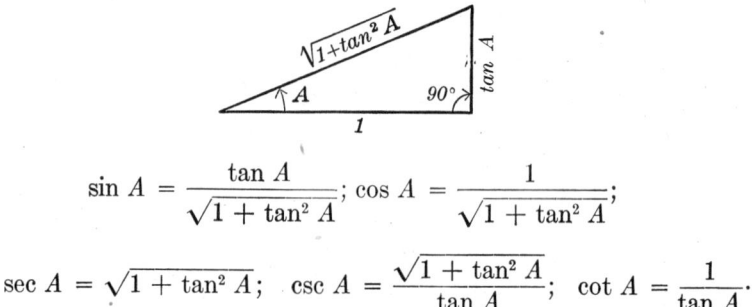

$$\sin A = \frac{\tan A}{\sqrt{1 + \tan^2 A}}; \cos A = \frac{1}{\sqrt{1 + \tan^2 A}};$$

$$\sec A = \sqrt{1 + \tan^2 A}; \csc A = \frac{\sqrt{1 + \tan^2 A}}{\tan A}; \cot A = \frac{1}{\tan A}.$$

3. Express $\tan A + \cot A$ in terms of sines and cosines.

$$\tan A + \cot A = \frac{\sin A}{\cos A} + \frac{\cos A}{\sin A} = \frac{\sin^2 A + \cos^2 A}{\sin A \cos A} = \frac{1}{\sin A \cos A}.$$

EXERCISES

1. Express $\cos A$ in terms of the other functions.
2. Express all the functions in terms of $\cos A$.
3. Express all the functions in terms of $\sec A$.

FUNDAMENTAL TRIGONOMETRIC RELATIONS

Verify the following identities. In the verification of identities it is urged that the left member be changed to read the same as the right member, or the reverse. Do not use the algebraic substitution to prove any identity; that is, do not substitute $\frac{a}{c}$ for sin A, etc.

4. $(1 - \sec^2 A)(1 - \csc^2 A) = 1$.
5. $\tan^2 A (\csc^2 A - 1) = 1$.
6. $\sin^2 A (1 + \cot^2 A) = 1$.
7. $\cot^2 A - \cos^2 A = \cot^2 A \cos^2 A$.
8. $\cos A \sin A (\cot A + \tan A) = 1$.
9. $\dfrac{1 + \cot^2 A}{1 + \tan^2 A} = \cot^2 A$.
10. $(\tan A - \cot A) \sin A \cos A = \sin^2 A - \cos^2 A$.
11. $\sqrt{\sec^2 A + \csc^2 A} = \tan A + \cot A$.
12. $\sec^4 A - \tan^4 A = \sec^2 A + \tan^2 A$.
13. $1 - \tan^4 A = 2 \sec^2 A - \sec^4 A$.
14. $\dfrac{1 + \cos A}{1 - \cos A} = (\csc A + \cot A)^2$.
15. $(\sin A + \cos A)^2 + (\sin A - \cos A)^2 = 2$.
16. $\dfrac{\cot A \cos A}{\cot A + \cos A} = \dfrac{\cot A - \cos A}{\cot A \cos A}$.
17. $\cot A \cos A + \sin A = \csc A$.
18. $\sin^3 A + \cos^3 A = (\sin A + \cos A)(1 - \sin A \cos A)$.
19. $\sin^6 A + \cos^6 A = 1 - 3 \sin^2 A \cos^2 A$.

38. Solving trigonometric equations

In a trigonometric equation the unknown is a *function of an angle*. The angle which reduces the equation to an identity is a *solution*. If several different functions of the angle are involved in the equation, the first step in the solution is to express all functions in terms of a single function.

EXAMPLES

1. Find the acute angle which is a solution of the equation sec A cot $A = \frac{4}{3}$.

The left member of the equation may be written
$$\frac{1}{\cos A} \times \frac{\cos A}{\sin A} = \frac{1}{\sin A}.$$

Then $\dfrac{1}{\sin A} = \frac{4}{3}$, or sin $A = \frac{3}{4} = .7500$. $A = 48° 36'$.

2. Solve the equation $2 \sin A = 2 - \cos A$.

The equation reduces to $2\sqrt{1 - \cos^2 A} = 2 - \cos A$. Squaring each member of this equation gives

$$4 - 4\cos^2 A = 4 - 4\cos A + \cos^2 A.$$

Rearranging, $\cos A (5 \cos A - 4) = 0.$
Then $\cos A = 0$ or $\cos A = \frac{4}{5}$.
$A = 90°$ or $36° 52'$.

3. Solve the equation $2 \tan^2 A - 5 \tan A + 3 = 0$.
   Factoring, $(\tan A - 1)(2 \tan A - 3) = 0$.
   Then $\tan A - 1 = 0$, or $2 \tan A - 3 = 0$.
   $\tan A = 1$, or $\tan A = \frac{3}{2} = 1.5$.
   $A = 45°$ or $56° 19'$.

EXERCISES

Find the angles to the nearest minute from 0° to 90° inclusive that are solutions of the equations. When square roots are to be found, use only the positive square root.

1. $2 \cos A = \sec A$.
2. $4 \sin A = 3 \csc A$.
3. $4 \cos A - 3 \sec A = 0$.
4. $\sqrt{2} \sin A - \tan A = 0$.
5. $\sin A - \cos A = 0$.
6. $3 \tan A - 4 \sin A = 0$.
7. $8 \cos^2 A = 10 \cos A - 3$.
8. $6 \sin^2 A - 5 \sin A + 1 = 0$.
9. $\tan A + 3 \cot A - 4 = 0$.
10. $\sec^2 A + \cos^2 A - 7 = 0$.
11. $\sin A + \cos A = \sec A$.
12. $\cos A = 2(1 - \sin A)$.
13. $\sin A + \sqrt{3} \cos A = 2$.
14. $\tan^2 A - 1 = 2(\sin^2 A - \cos^2 A)$.
15. $2 \cos A + \sec A = 3$.

In the exercises and applications thus far studied we have used only the functions of a single angle. There are many kinds of exercises in which it is convenient to consider the functions of two or more angles. The fundamental relations which will be developed in the next sections have many important uses and applications.

FUNDAMENTAL TRIGONOMETRIC RELATIONS

39. Sine of the sum of two angles

The sine of the sum of two angles is equal to the sine of the first angle times the cosine of the second angle, plus the cosine of the first angle times the sine of the second angle.

$$\sin(A + B) = \sin A \cos B + \cos A \sin B.$$

Proof: In the figures, $\angle XOY = A$ and $\angle YOZ = B$. Then $\angle XOZ = (A + B)$.

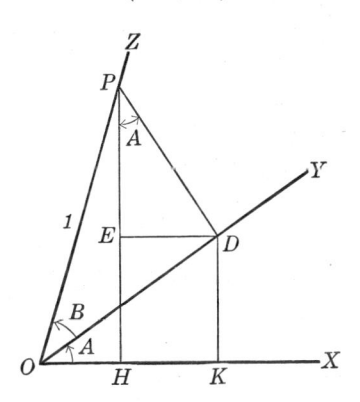

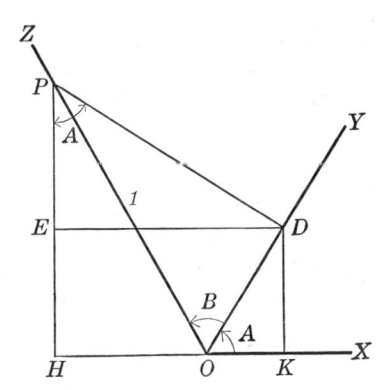

On OZ mark off a distance $OP = 1$. Draw PH perpendicular to OX and PD perpendicular to OY. KD is perpendicular to OX, and ED is perpendicular to HP. $\angle EPD = A$. Why?

$\sin(A + B) = HP = HE + EP = KD + EP$.

In the triangle OKD, $KD = OD \sin A$. Why?
In the triangle DEP, $EP = DP \cos A$. Why?

$\sin(A + B) = OD \sin A + DP \cos A$.

In the triangle ODP, $OD = \cos B$, and $DP = \sin B$.

$\sin(A + B) = \sin A \cos B + \cos A \sin B$.

EXAMPLE

$\sin(30° + 45°) = \sin 75° = \sin 30° \cos 45° + \cos 30° \sin 45°$.

$$\sin 75° = \frac{1}{2} \times \frac{1}{\sqrt{2}} + \frac{\sqrt{3}}{2} \times \frac{1}{\sqrt{2}} = \frac{1}{2\sqrt{2}} + \frac{\sqrt{3}}{2\sqrt{2}} = \frac{1 + \sqrt{3}}{2\sqrt{2}}.$$

$$\sin 75° = \frac{1 + \sqrt{3}}{2\sqrt{2}} = \frac{1 + \sqrt{3}}{2\sqrt{2}} \times \frac{\sqrt{2}}{\sqrt{2}} = \frac{\sqrt{2} + \sqrt{6}}{4} = .9659.$$

Find $\sin 75°$ in the tables. Is the above answer correct?

40. Cosine of the sum of two angles

The cosine of the sum of two angles is equal to the cosine of the first angle times the cosine of the second angle, minus the sine of the first angle times the sine of the second angle.

$$\cos(A + B) = \cos A \cos B - \sin A \sin B.$$

Proof: See the figure on page 83.
$$\cos(A + B) = OH = OK - HK = OK - ED.$$
In the second figure $HO = ED - OK$; $-HO = OK - ED$; $OH = OK - ED.$
In the triangle OKD, $OK = OD \cos A.$
In the triangle DEP, $ED = DP \sin A.$
$\cos(A + B) = OD \cos A - DP \sin A = \cos A \cos B - \sin A \sin B.$

Example

$\cos(30° + 45°) = \cos 75° = \cos 30° \cos 45° - \sin 30° \sin 45°.$

$$\cos 75° = \frac{\sqrt{3}}{2} \times \frac{1}{\sqrt{2}} - \frac{1}{2} \times \frac{1}{\sqrt{2}}.$$

$$\cos 75° = \frac{\sqrt{3} - 1}{2\sqrt{2}} = \frac{\sqrt{6} - \sqrt{2}}{4} = .2588.$$

Find $\cos 75°$ in the tables. Is the above answer correct?

Caution: The sine of the sum of two angles is *not equal* to the sum of the sines of the angles. The cosine of the sum of two angles is *not equal* to the sum of the cosines of the angles. See figures on page 83.

EXERCISES

1. Since $\sin 60° = \sin(30° + 30°)$, show that $\sin 60° = \frac{\sqrt{3}}{2}$.
2. Show similarly that $\cos 60° = \frac{1}{2}$.
3. Since $120° = 60° + 60°$, show that $\sin 120° = \frac{\sqrt{3}}{2} = \sin 60°$.
4. Show similarly that $\cos 120° = -\frac{1}{2} = -\cos 60°$.
5. Since $150° = 120° + 30°$, show that $\sin 150° = \frac{1}{2} = \sin 30°$.
6. Show that $\cos 150° = -\frac{\sqrt{3}}{2} = -\cos 30°$.
7. Does $\sin 15° = \sin 8° + \sin 7°$?
Does $\cos 40° = \cos 30° + \cos 10°$?

FUNDAMENTAL TRIGONOMETRIC RELATIONS

EXAMPLE

Given $\sin A = \frac{3}{5}$ and $\sin B = \frac{5}{13}$. Find $\sin (A + B)$ and $\cos (A + B)$. Then find the angle $(A + B)$.

First construct the scale triangle for each angle.

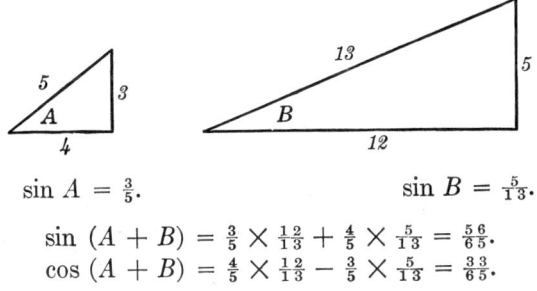

$\sin A = \frac{3}{5}.$ $\qquad\qquad\qquad \sin B = \frac{5}{13}.$

$\sin (A + B) = \frac{3}{5} \times \frac{12}{13} + \frac{4}{5} \times \frac{5}{13} = \frac{56}{65}.$
$\cos (A + B) = \frac{4}{5} \times \frac{12}{13} - \frac{3}{5} \times \frac{5}{13} = \frac{33}{65}.$

Since the sine and the cosine of the sum of A and B are positive, $(A + B)$ is an acute angle.

$\sin (A + B) = \frac{56}{65} = .8615.$
$(A + B) = 59° \, 29'.$

EXERCISES

1. Given $\sin A = \frac{3}{5}$ and $\cos B = \frac{15}{17}$. Show that $\sin (A + B) = \frac{77}{85}$. Find $(A + B)$ in degrees. $\cos (A + B) = ?$

2. Given $\cos A = \dfrac{\sqrt{3}}{2}$ and $\cos B = \dfrac{1}{3}$. Show that $\sin (A + B) = \dfrac{1 + 2\sqrt{6}}{6}$. Also show that $\cos (A + B) = \dfrac{\sqrt{3} - 2\sqrt{2}}{6}$. Is $(A + B)$ acute or obtuse? Why?

3. Given $\tan A = \dfrac{1}{2}$ and $\sin B = \dfrac{1}{\sqrt{10}}$. Show that $(A + B) = 45°$.

4. Given $\sin A = \frac{3}{5}$ and $\cos B = -\frac{1}{2}$, (B is obtuse). Is $(A + B)$ acute or obtuse? Why?

41. Tangent of the sum of two angles

The tangent of the sum of two angles is equal to a fraction whose numerator is the sum of the tangents of the two angles and whose denominator is 1 minus the product of the tangents.

$$\tan (A + B) = \frac{\tan A + \tan B}{1 - \tan A \tan B}.$$

Proof: We have learned that the tangent of an angle is equal to the sine of the angle divided by the cosine of the angle. We have also developed expressions for sin $(A + B)$ and cos $(A + B)$. Then

$$\tan (A + B) = \frac{\sin (A + B)}{\cos (A + B)} = \frac{\sin A \cos B + \cos A \sin B}{\cos A \cos B - \sin A \sin B}.$$

Divide each term of the numerator and denominator of the fraction by $\cos A \cos B$.

$$\tan (A + B) = \frac{\dfrac{\sin A}{\cos A} + \dfrac{\sin B}{\cos B}}{1 - \dfrac{\sin A \sin B}{\cos A \cos B}} = \frac{\tan A + \tan B}{1 - \tan A \tan B}.$$

EXAMPLE

$$\tan (30° + 45°) = \tan 75° = \frac{\dfrac{1}{\sqrt{3}} + 1}{1 - \dfrac{1}{\sqrt{3}}} = \frac{\sqrt{3} + 1}{\sqrt{3} - 1} = 3.7321.$$

Find tan 75° in the tables. Is the above answer correct?

Caution: The tangent of the sum of two angles is *not equal* to the sum of the tangents of the angles.

EXERCISES

1. Since $30° + 30° = 60°$, show that $\tan 60° = \sqrt{3}$.
2. Using $60° + 60° = 120°$, show that $\tan 120° = -\sqrt{3} = -\tan 60°$.
3. Using $120° + 30° = 150°$, show that $\tan 150° = -\dfrac{1}{\sqrt{3}} = -\tan 30°$.
4. Given $\tan A = \frac{1}{2}$ and $\tan B = \frac{1}{3}$, show that $(A + B) = 45°$.
5. Given $\tan A = \frac{1}{3}$ and $\tan B = 1$, show that $\tan (A + B) = 2$.
6. Given $\tan A = \frac{3}{2}$ and $\tan B = \frac{3}{4}$, show that $\tan (A + B) = -18$. Is $(A + B)$ acute or obtuse? Why?
7. Given $\tan A = \frac{5}{6}$ and $\tan B = \frac{1}{11}$. Show that $(A + B) = 45°$.
8. Give a geometrical proof for the expression of the tangent of the sum of two angles. See the figure on page 83.

42. Sine of the difference of two angles

The sine of the difference of two angles is equal to the sine of the first angle times the cosine of the second angle, minus the cosine of the first angle times the sine of the second angle.

$$\sin (A - B) = \sin A \cos B - \cos A \sin B.$$

Proof: The proof is given only for A and B acute. Later it

FUNDAMENTAL TRIGONOMETRIC RELATIONS

will be shown that the theorem is true for all values of A and B.

In the figure $\angle XOY = A$, $\angle YOZ = B$, and $\angle XOZ = (A - B)$.

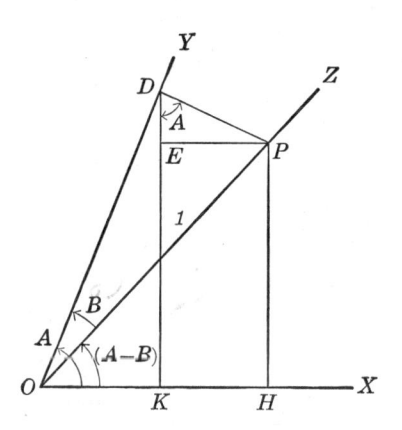

On OZ mark off $OP = 1$. PD is perpendicular to OY; PH is perpendicular to OX; KD is parallel to HP; and EP is parallel to OX. Then $\angle EDP = A$. Why?
$$\sin(A - B) = HP = KD - ED.$$
In the triangle OKD, $KD = OD \sin A$.
In the triangle DEP, $ED = DP \cos A$.
$$\sin(A - B) = OD \sin A - DP \cos A.$$
In the triangle ODP, $OD = \cos B$ and $DP = \sin B$.
$$\sin(A - B) = \sin A \cos B - \cos A \sin B.$$

Example

$$\sin(60° - 45°) = \sin 15° = \frac{\sqrt{3}}{2} \times \frac{1}{\sqrt{2}} - \frac{1}{2} \times \frac{1}{\sqrt{2}}.$$

$$\sin 15° = \frac{\sqrt{3} - 1}{2\sqrt{2}} = \frac{\sqrt{6} - \sqrt{2}}{4} = .2588.$$

Find sin 15° in the tables. Is the above answer correct?

Caution: The sine of the difference of two angles is *not equal* to the difference of the sines of the angles. See figure above.

EXERCISE

Given $\sin A = \frac{4}{5}$ and $\sin B = \frac{3}{5}$, A and B both acute. Show that $\sin(A - B) = \frac{7}{25}$. Find $(A - B)$.

43. Cosine of the difference of two angles

The cosine of the difference of two angles is equal to the cosine of the first angle times the cosine of the second angle, plus the sine of the first angle times the sine of the second angle.

$$\cos(A - B) = \cos A \cos B + \sin A \sin B.$$

Proof: See the figure on page 87.
$\cos(A - B) = OH = OK + KH = OK + EP.$
In the triangle OKD, $OK = OD \cos A$.
In the triangle DEP, $EP = DP \sin A$.
$\cos(A - B) = OD \cos A + DP \sin A.$
$OD = \cos B$, and $DP = \sin B$.
$\cos(A - B) = \cos A \cos B + \sin A \sin B.$

EXAMPLE

$$\cos(45° - 30°) = \cos 15° = \frac{1}{\sqrt{2}} \times \frac{\sqrt{3}}{2} + \frac{1}{\sqrt{2}} \times \frac{1}{2}.$$

$$\cos 15° = \frac{\sqrt{3} + 1}{2\sqrt{2}} = \frac{\sqrt{6} + \sqrt{2}}{4} = .9659.$$

Find $\cos 15°$ in the tables and see whether the above answer is correct.

Caution: The cosine of the difference of two angles is *not equal* to the difference of the cosines of the angles. See figure, page 87.

EXERCISE

Given $\sin A = \frac{4}{5}$ and $\cos B = \frac{4}{5}$, A and B both acute. Show that $\cos(A - B) = \frac{24}{25}$. Find $(A - B)$.

44. Tangent of the difference of two angles

The tangent of the difference of two angles is equal to a fraction whose numerator is the difference of the tangents of the angles, and whose denominator is 1 plus the product of the tangents.

$$\tan(A - B) = \frac{\tan A - \tan B}{1 + \tan A \tan B}.$$

Proof:

$$\tan(A - B) = \frac{\sin(A - B)}{\cos(A - B)} = \frac{\sin A \cos B - \cos A \sin B}{\cos A \cos B + \sin A \sin B}.$$

Divide each term of the last fraction by $(\cos A \cos B)$.

FUNDAMENTAL TRIGONOMETRIC RELATIONS

$$\tan(A - B) = \frac{\dfrac{\sin A}{\cos A} - \dfrac{\sin B}{\cos B}}{1 + \dfrac{\sin A \sin B}{\cos A \cos B}} = \frac{\tan A - \tan B}{1 + \tan A \tan B}$$

EXAMPLES

1. $\tan(60° - 45°) = \tan 15° = \dfrac{\sqrt{3} - 1}{1 + \sqrt{3}} = 2 - \sqrt{3} = .2679$

2. $\tan(135° - 30°) = \tan 105° = \dfrac{-1 - \dfrac{1}{\sqrt{3}}}{1 - \dfrac{1}{\sqrt{3}}} = -2 - \sqrt{3}$.

$\tan 105° = -\tan 75° = -3.7321$. In the tables find $\tan 15°$ and $\tan 75°$. Are the above answers correct?

Caution: The tangent of the difference of two angles is *not* equal to the difference of the tangents of the angles.

EXERCISES

1. Given $\tan A = \frac{1}{2}$ and $\tan B = \frac{1}{3}$, show that $\tan(A - B) = \frac{1}{7}$. Find $(A - B)$.

2. When $\cos A = \frac{3}{5}$ and $\sin B = \frac{3}{5}$, show that $\tan(A - B) = \frac{7}{24}$. Find $(A - B)$.

3. Given $A = 135°$ and $\sin B = \frac{5}{13}$ (B acute), show that $\tan(A - B) = -\frac{17}{7}$. Is $(A - B)$ acute or obtuse? Why?

4. Given $\tan A = \frac{3}{4}$, $\tan B = \frac{3}{5}$, and $\tan C = \frac{8}{19}$ (A, B, and C acute), show that $(A + B - C) = 45°$.

5. Give a geometrical proof of the tangent of the difference of two angles. See figure, page 87.

45. Functions of 0°, 90°, and 180°

$\sin 0° = 0.$ $\sin 90° = 1.$ $\sin 180° = 0.$
$\cos 0° = 1.$ $\cos 90° = 0.$ $\cos 180° = -1.$
$\tan 0° = 0.$ $\tan 90° = \infty.$ $\tan 180° = 0.$
$\cot 0° = \infty.$ $\cot 90° = 0.$ $\cot 180° = \infty.$

Show that $\sin 0° = 0$:

$$\sin 0° = \sin(30° - 30°) = \frac{1}{2} \times \frac{\sqrt{3}}{2} - \frac{\sqrt{3}}{2} \times \frac{1}{2} = 0.$$

Show that $\cot 0° = \infty$: See discussion on page 30.

$$\tan 0° = 0. \quad \cot 0° = \frac{1}{\tan 0°} = \frac{1}{0} = \infty.$$

Note: When the divisor is 0, the quotient is indefinite and infinitely large and called *infinity*. The symbol for infinity is ∞.

Show that $\sin 90° = 1$:

$$\sin 90° = \sin(45° + 45°) = \frac{1}{\sqrt{2}} \times \frac{1}{\sqrt{2}} + \frac{1}{\sqrt{2}} \times \frac{1}{\sqrt{2}} = \frac{1}{2} + \frac{1}{2} = 1.$$

Show that $\cot 90° = 0$:

$$\tan 90° = \infty. \quad \cot 90° = \frac{1}{\tan 90°} = \frac{1}{\infty} = 0.$$

Note: When the divisor is indefinitely large, the quotient is considered 0.

Show that $\cos 180° = -1$:

$$\cos 180° = \cos(90° + 90°) = 0 \times 0 - 1 \times 1 = -1.$$

EXERCISES

1. Find the functions of 0° by using (45° − 45°).
2. Find the functions of 90° by using (60° + 30°).
3. Find the functions of 180° by using (150° + 30°).
4. Show that $\sin(A + B) + \sin(A - B) = 2 \sin A \cos B$.
5. Show that $\cos(A - B) - \cos(A + B) = 2 \sin A \sin B$.
6. **Prove** that $\tan 45° + \tan 45°$ *does not equal* $\tan 90°$.
7. **Prove** that $\sin 60° + \sin 30°$ *does not equal* $\sin 90°$.
8. **Prove** that $\cos 120° - \cos 30°$ *does not equal* $\cos 90°$.

46. Functions of twice an angle

Formulas for the sine, the cosine, and the tangent of the sum of two angles have been developed. By assuming the two angles are equal, we can find the functions of twice an angle in terms of the functions of the angle.

The sine of twice an angle is equal to two times the product of the sine of the angle and the cosine of the angle.

$$\sin 2A = 2 \sin A \cos A.$$

Proof: We know that $\sin(A + B) = \sin A \cos B + \cos A \sin B$.
Let $B = A$; then $\sin 2A = \sin A \cos A + \cos A \sin A$.

$$\sin 2A = 2 \sin A \cos A.$$

EXAMPLES

1. $\sin 60° = \sin(2 \times 30°) = 2 \sin 30° \cos 30° = 2 \times \frac{1}{2} \times \frac{\sqrt{3}}{2} = \frac{\sqrt{3}}{2}.$

2. $\sin 90° = \sin(2 \times 45°) = 2 \sin 45° \cos 45° = 2 \times \frac{1}{\sqrt{2}} \times \frac{1}{\sqrt{2}} = 1.$

FUNDAMENTAL TRIGONOMETRIC RELATIONS

The cosine of twice an angle is equal to the square of the cosine of the angle minus the square of the sine of the angle.

$$\cos 2A = \cos^2 A - \sin^2 A.$$

Proof: $\cos (A + B) = \cos A \cos B - \sin A \sin B$. Let $B = A$.
Then $\cos 2A = \cos A \cos A - \sin A \sin A$.
$$\cos 2A = \cos^2 A - \sin^2 A.$$

Show that
$$\cos 2A = 1 - 2 \sin^2 A \text{ and } \cos 2A = 2 \cos^2 A - 1.$$

EXAMPLES

1. $\cos 60° = \cos (2 \times 30°) = \cos^2 30° - \sin^2 30° = \dfrac{3}{4} - \dfrac{1}{4} = \dfrac{1}{2}.$

2. $\cos 90° = \cos (2 \times 45°) = \cos^2 45° - \sin^2 45° = \dfrac{1}{2} - \dfrac{1}{2} = 0.$

The tangent of twice an angle is equal to a fraction whose numerator is twice the tangent of the angle, and whose denominator is 1 minus the square of the tangent of the angle.

$$\tan 2A = \frac{2 \tan A}{1 - \tan^2 A}.$$

Proof:

$$\tan (A + B) = \frac{\tan A + \tan B}{1 - \tan A \tan B}. \quad \text{Let } B = A.$$

Then the result is easily obtained.

EXAMPLES

1. $\tan 60° = \tan (2 \times 30°) = \dfrac{2 \tan 30°}{1 - \tan^2 30°} = \dfrac{2 \times \frac{1}{\sqrt{3}}}{1 - \frac{1}{3}} = \dfrac{3}{\sqrt{3}} = \sqrt{3}.$

2. $\tan 120° = \tan (2 \times 60°) = \dfrac{2 \tan 60°}{1 - \tan^2 60°} = \dfrac{2 \times \sqrt{3}}{1 - 3} = -\sqrt{3}.$

Caution: The sine of twice an angle is *not equal* to twice the sine of the angle. The same is true for the cosine and tangent of twice an angle.

EXERCISES

1. Find the sine of 120° using the functions of 60°.
2. Find sin 180° and cos 180° using the functions of 90°.
3. Given $\sin A = \frac{3}{5}$, A being acute, find sin 2A, cos 2A, and tan 2A. Find 2A in degrees.
4. Given $\cos A = \frac{5}{13}$, A being acute, find sin 2A, cos 2A, and tan 2A. Find 2A in degrees.

5. Given $\tan A = \frac{1}{2}$, find $\sin 2A$, $\cos 2A$, and $\tan 2A$.

6. When $\tan \dfrac{A}{2} = \frac{1}{7}$, find $\tan A$. Find A in degrees.

7. When $\tan \dfrac{A}{2} = 2$, find $\tan A$. Find A in degrees.

8. If $\sin 2A = \frac{1}{3}$, $2A$ being acute, find $\sin 4A$. Find A in degrees.
9. If $\sin 3X = \frac{5}{13}$, $3X$ being acute, find $\sin 6X$.
10. When $\sin 4B = \frac{1}{5}$, $4B$ being acute, find $\sin 8B$.
11. Show that $\sin 3A = 3 \sin A - 4 \sin^3 A$.
 Hint: $\sin 3A = \sin (2A + A)$.
12. Show that $\cos 3A = 4 \cos^3 A - 3 \cos A$.
13. Given $\sin A = \frac{3}{5}$, $\sin B = \frac{5}{13}$, A and B both acute, find $\sin (2A + 2B)$.
14. Using the functions of twice an angle, verify the numbers in this table.

Note: Remember that a finite number divided by 0 is represented by ∞.

	sin	cos	tan	cot
90°	1	0	∞	0
180°	0	-1	0	∞

47. Functions of half an angle

You have learned that $\cos 2X = \cos^2 X - \sin^2 X$. See page 91. Let $2X = A$. Then $\cos A = \cos^2 \dfrac{A}{2} - \sin^2 \dfrac{A}{2}$. Since $\sin^2 \dfrac{A}{2} + \cos^2 \dfrac{A}{2} = 1$, we may write

$$\cos A = 1 - 2 \sin^2 \dfrac{A}{2}, \qquad (1)$$

or $\cos A = 2 \cos^2 \dfrac{A}{2} - 1.$ \qquad (2)

From (1) we get

$$\sin \dfrac{A}{2} = \sqrt{\dfrac{1 - \cos A}{2}}. \qquad (3)$$

From (2) we get

$$\cos \dfrac{A}{2} = \sqrt{\dfrac{1 + \cos A}{2}}. \qquad (4)$$

FUNDAMENTAL TRIGONOMETRIC RELATIONS

Dividing (3) by (4) gives

$$\tan\frac{A}{2} = \sqrt{\frac{1 - \cos A}{1 + \cos A}}. \tag{5}$$

We determine the sign by the quadrant in which $\frac{A}{2}$ lies. It is plus if A is acute. See Chapter VI for other cases.

EXAMPLES

1. $\sin 30° = \sqrt{\frac{1 - \cos 60°}{2}} = \sqrt{\frac{1 - \frac{1}{2}}{2}} = \sqrt{\frac{1}{4}} = \frac{1}{2}.$

2. $\cos 22\frac{1}{2}° = \sqrt{\frac{1 + \cos 45°}{2}} = \sqrt{\frac{1 + \frac{1}{\sqrt{2}}}{2}} = \frac{1}{2}\sqrt{2 + \sqrt{2}} = .9238.$

3. When $\cos A = \frac{3}{5}$, A being acute, $\tan\frac{A}{2} = \sqrt{\frac{1 - \frac{3}{5}}{1 + \frac{3}{5}}} = \frac{1}{2}.$

Caution: The sine of one-half an angle is *not equal* to one-half of the sine of the angle. The same is true for the cosine and tangent of one-half an angle.

EXERCISES

Consider only positive roots.

1. When $\sin A = \frac{5}{13}$, A being acute, find $\tan\frac{A}{2}$. *Hint:* Draw the scale right triangle for the given function.

2. When $\sin A = \frac{3}{5}$, A being acute, find $\sin\frac{A}{2}$, $\cos\frac{A}{2}$, and $\tan\frac{A}{2}$.

3. When $\sin A = \frac{4}{5}$, A being obtuse, find $\tan\frac{A}{2}$.

4. Given $\tan 2A = \frac{4}{3}$, find $\sin A$, $\cos A$, and $\tan A$. Find A in degrees.

5. If $\tan 2A = 1$, A is how many degrees?

6. If $\cos 4B = \frac{5}{13}$, find $\sin 2B$.

7. If $\sin 8X = \frac{1}{2}$, find $\sin 4X$.

8. When $\sin\frac{A}{2} = \frac{7}{25}$, find $\sin\frac{A}{4}$.

9. Show that $\tan 22\frac{1}{2}° = \sqrt{\frac{\sqrt{2} - 1}{\sqrt{2} + 1}} = \sqrt{2} - 1.$

10. Show that $\sin 15° = \frac{1}{2}\sqrt{2 - \sqrt{3}} = \frac{\sqrt{6} - \sqrt{2}}{4} = .2588.$

11. Show that $\cos 15° = \frac{1}{2}\sqrt{2 + \sqrt{3}} = \frac{\sqrt{6} + \sqrt{2}}{4} = .9659$.

12. Show that $\tan 15° = 2 - \sqrt{3} = .2679$.

48. Sum and difference of the same function of two angles

In many kinds of problems and exercises we meet the need of using the sum or the difference of the same function of two angles. Because of the ease of computation, it is advisable to change the sum or the difference into a product.

Note: Before developing further relations between the functions of angles, it is important to know that the relations developed on pages 83, 84, 85, 86, 88, 90, 91, 92, and the relations on this page, hold for angles of any size. In a later chapter angles greater than 360° are considered.

If X and Y are the angles, then

$$\sin (X + Y) = \sin X \cos Y + \cos X \sin Y. \tag{1}$$
$$\sin (X - Y) = \sin X \cos Y - \cos X \sin Y. \tag{2}$$

Adding (1) and (2) gives

$$\sin (X + Y) + \sin (X - Y) = 2 \sin X \cos Y. \tag{3}$$

Subtracting (2) from (1) gives

$$\sin (X + Y) - \sin (X - Y) = 2 \cos X \sin Y. \tag{4}$$

It is possible to choose angles A and B so that $X + Y = A$ and $X - Y = B$. Solving these two equations for X and Y in terms of A and B, we get

$$X = \frac{A + B}{2} \text{ and } Y = \frac{A - B}{2}.$$

Substituting these values of X and Y in (3) and (4) gives

$$\sin A + \sin B = 2 \sin \frac{A + B}{2} \cos \frac{A - B}{2}. \tag{5}$$

$$\sin A - \sin B = 2 \cos \frac{A + B}{2} \sin \frac{A - B}{2}. \tag{6}$$

In a similar manner, using $\cos (X + Y)$ and $\cos (X - Y)$, we are able to derive

$$\cos A + \cos B = 2 \cos \frac{A + B}{2} \cos \frac{A - B}{2}. \tag{7}$$

$$\cos A - \cos B = -2 \sin \frac{A + B}{2} \sin \frac{A - B}{2}. \tag{8}$$

FUNDAMENTAL TRIGONOMETRIC RELATIONS

EXAMPLE

Express $\sin 50° + \sin 30°$ as a product. Use (5), page 94.

$$\sin 50° + \sin 30° = 2 \sin \frac{50° + 30°}{2} \cos \frac{50° - 30°}{2} = 2 \sin 40° \cos 10°.$$

EXERCISES

1. Show that $\sin 60° + \sin 30° = 2 \sin 45° \cos 15° = \sqrt{2} \cos 15°$.
2. Prove: $\sin 40° + \sin 20° = \cos 10°$.
3. Prove: $\cos 75° + \cos 45° = \cos 15°$.
4. Prove: $\sin 120° + \sin 60° = \sqrt{3}$.
5. Prove: $\cos 75° - \cos 15° = -\frac{1}{2}\sqrt{2}$.
6. Prove: $\sin 50° - \sin 40° = \sqrt{2} \sin 5°$.
7. Prove: $\sin 150° + \sin 60° = \frac{1}{2}(1 + \sqrt{3})$.

49. Solving more difficult trigonometric equations

EXERCISES

Solve the following equations, finding all solutions from 0° to 180°, and expressing the angles to the nearest minute.

1. $\sin 2A = \cos A$. *Hint:* Express $\sin 2A$ in terms of functions of A.
2. $\sin A = \cos 2A$. *Hint:* Use $\cos 2A = 1 - 2 \sin^2 A$.
3. $\cos 3A = \sin 2A$. See exercise 12, page 92.
4. $\cos 3A + 2 \cos A = 0$.
5. $5 \sin A + 12 \cos A = 8$. One method for solving this equation is to express one function in terms of the other function, and then free the resulting equation of radicals.

Solution by a special method. The plan of this method is to arrange the left member of the given equation in the form of $\sin A \cos B \pm \cos A \sin B$. To do this, we assume $\tan B = \frac{12}{5}$. Then it follows that $\sin B = \frac{12}{13}$ and $\cos B = \frac{5}{13}$. Divide each member of the given equation by $\sqrt{5^2 + 12^2}$ or 13.

$$\sin A \tfrac{5}{13} + \cos A \tfrac{12}{13} = \tfrac{8}{13}.$$
$$\sin A \cos B + \cos A \sin B = \tfrac{8}{13}.$$
$$\sin (A + B) = \tfrac{8}{13} = .6154.$$
$$A + B = 37° 59' \text{ or } 142° 1'.$$
$$\tan B = \tfrac{12}{5} = 2.4, \ B = 67° 22'.$$

It is evident that $(A + B)$ cannot be $37° 59'$. Hence,
$$A = 142° 1' - 67° 22' = 74° 39'.$$

6. $3 \sin A + 4 \cos A = 2$.

7. $5 \sin A - 2 \cos A = 3$.
8. $2.45 \sin A - 5.75 \cos A = 3.5$.
9. $15 \sin A + 8 \cos A = 8.5$.
10. $5 \sin A - 12 \cos A = \dfrac{13\sqrt{3}}{2}$.

Find all the angles from 0° to 180° inclusive which will satisfy the following equations.

11. $4 \sec^2 A - 7 \tan^2 A = 3$.
12. $2 \sin A = 1 + \cos A$.
13. $\tan A \sec A = \sqrt{2}$.
14. $2 \cos^2 A + 3 \sin 2A - 2 = 0$.
15. $\sin A \cos A = -\dfrac{\sqrt{3}}{4}$.
16. $6 \cos^2 \dfrac{A}{2} + \cos 2A = 4$.
17. $\sin 3A + \sin A = 0$. *Hint:* Use (5), page 94.

50. Miscellaneous identities

Remember that in verifying identities it is convenient to transform the left member by the use of known identities to read the same as the right member, or the reverse.

EXERCISES

Verify the following identities.

1. $\tan A + \tan B = \dfrac{\sin (A + B)}{\cos A \cos B}$. *Hint:* Express the tangents in terms of sines and cosines.
2. $\tan A - \tan B = \dfrac{\sin (A - B)}{\cos A \cos B}$.
3. (a) $\sin (90° + A) = \cos A$. (b) $\cos (90° + A) = -\sin A$.
4. (a) $\sin (180° - A) = \sin A$. (c) $\cos (180° - A) = -\cos A$.
   (b) $\sin (180° + A) = -\sin A$. (d) $\cos (180° + A) = -\cos A$.
5. $\dfrac{\tan A - \tan B}{\tan A + \tan B} = \dfrac{\sin (A - B)}{\sin (A + B)}$.
6. $\cos (A - B) \cos (A + B) = \cos^2 A - \sin^2 B$.
7. $\sin (A - B) \sin (A + B) = \sin^2 A - \sin^2 B$.
8. $\sin 2A = \dfrac{2 \tan A}{1 + \tan^2 A}$.
9. $\cos 2A = \dfrac{1 - \tan^2 A}{1 + \tan^2 A}$.

FUNDAMENTAL TRIGONOMETRIC RELATIONS

10. $\dfrac{\sin 75° - \sin 15°}{\cos 75° + \cos 15°} = \tan 30°.$

11. $\dfrac{\sin A + \sin B}{\sin A - \sin B} = \dfrac{\tan \frac{1}{2}(A+B)}{\tan \frac{1}{2}(A-B)}.$

12. $\sin 80° \sin 60° \sin 40° \sin 20° = \frac{3}{16}.$

13. When $\cos A = -\frac{12}{13}$ (A is obtuse), find $\sin 2A$, $\cos 2A$, $\tan \dfrac{A}{2}$.

When A, B, and C are the angles of a triangle, verify the following exercises.

14. $\sin A + \sin B + \sin C = 4 \cos\left(\dfrac{A}{2}\right) \cos\left(\dfrac{B}{2}\right) \cos\left(\dfrac{C}{2}\right).$

15. $\tan A + \tan B + \tan C = \tan A \tan B \tan C.$

16. $\sin 2A + \sin 2B + \sin 2C = 4 \sin A \sin B \sin C.$

REVIEW QUESTIONS ON CHAPTER V

1. Write the six reciprocal functions of an angle.
2. Write the Pythagorean relations of the functions of an angle.
3. Express $\tan A$ and $\cot A$ in terms of $\sin A$; in terms of $\cos A$.
4. Prove the following: (a) $\tan A \csc A = \sec A$;

   (b) $\dfrac{\sin X + \csc Y}{\csc X + \sin Y} = \dfrac{\sin X}{\sin Y}$;   (c) $\dfrac{\sin^2 A}{\tan^2 A} + \dfrac{\cos^2 A}{\cot^2 A} = 1.$

5. Complete the following.

(a) $\sin(A+B) =$ (d) $\sin(A-B) =$ (g) $\sin 2A =$ (j) $\sin \dfrac{A}{2} =$

(b) $\cos(A+B) =$ (e) $\cos(A-B) =$ (h) $\cos 2A =$ (k) $\cos \dfrac{A}{2} =$

(c) $\tan(A+B) =$ (f) $\tan(A-B) =$ (i) $\tan 2A =$ (l) $\tan \dfrac{A}{2} =$

6. Develop each of the fundamental relations of exercise 5.
7. Solve the following equations:
   (a) $\sin A + \cos^2 A = 1.$
   (b) $\tan A + \sec A = 3.$
   (c) $\dfrac{1}{\sin^2 A} + \dfrac{1}{\cos^2 A} = 4.$

Graphs of the Trigonometric Functions

THE graphs of the trigonometric functions exhibit their periodic nature very clearly. Let us consider the sine curve on page 107. It is easily seen that the variation of the function from 0 to 2π is repeated from 2π to 4π, from 4π to 6π, and so on. Then we say that the sine has a *period* of 2π. The periods of the other functions can be readily determined from their graphs.

Examples of periodic phenomena are found in the motion of a pendulum, of a vibrating tuning fork, of the particles of water in a wave, of pistons which turn wheels. Thus it can be seen that as the trigonometric functions are periodic, they must be used in describing the motions of periodic phenomena.

The nature of the inverse function is also effectively exhibited by the graph. In later courses the student may meet another notation for this function. In this text the notation, $\sin^{-1} x$, $\cos^{-1} x$, etc., is used. This is called the English notation because John Herschel, an Englishman, used it in a publication in 1813, and it met with favor in England.

Another notation which expresses the same idea is arcsin x, arccos x, etc. This is called the continental notation, because it was first used in Continental Europe.

The rival notations still exist. In the United States prior to the present century, the English notation was used more extensively. In recent years some textbook writers are using the continental form.

CHAPTER
VI

Trigonometric Functions of Any Angle in Terms of the Functions of an Acute Angle

Graphs

THUS far we have met only exercises dealing with the functions of angles from 0° to 180°. In many types of exercises it is necessary that we know the functions of angles greater than 180°.

51. Trigonometric functions of any angle

We have learned to consider an angle as formed by a revolving line. Choose the X-axis as the initial position of the revolving line, and OR the terminal side of the generated angle XOR, or angle A. We wish to represent the scale right triangle associated

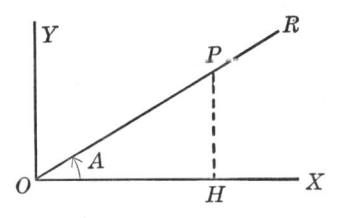

with the angle A. See page 15. Let P be any point in the terminal side of the angle A. Let HP be the perpendicular from the point P to the initial side which is the X-axis. Then the angle A has

99

the associated scale triangle OHP. The four cases which arise for the angles between 0° and 360° (90°, 180°, and 270° excepted) appear in the figures. The angle HOP always is acute.

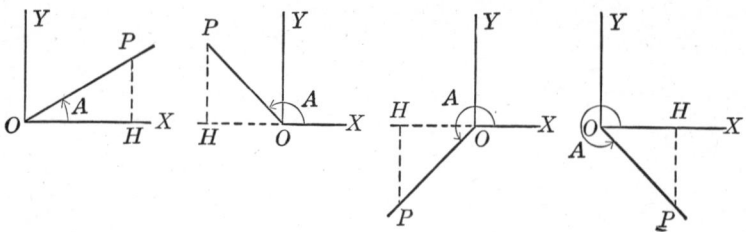

The coördinates of the point P are (x,y). Let d represent the number of units in the hypotenuse of the scale triangle HOP. In Chapter II you have learned that the six functions of any angle A are defined as follows:

$$\sin A = \frac{y}{d}. \qquad \cos A = \frac{x}{d}.$$
$$\tan A = \frac{y}{x}. \qquad \cot A = \frac{x}{y}.$$
$$\sec A = \frac{d}{x}. \qquad \csc A = \frac{d}{y}.$$

The value of d is positive, but the signs of x and y are determined by the position of the point P with reference to the quadrant in which the rotating line terminates.

Also you have learned in Chapter II that the continued rotation of OP beyond 360° will give no new position of the terminal side, hence no new functional values.

52. Signs of the functions in the four quadrants

Keeping in mind the signs of the coördinates x and y in the different quadrants, we conclude that for an angle which has its terminal side in

Quadrant I, all the functions are positive.
Quadrant II, the sine and cosecant are positive, and the other four functions are negative.
Quadrant III, the tangent and cotangent are positive, and the other four functions are negative.
Quadrant IV, the cosine and secant are positive, and the other four functions are negative.

Functions of 270° and 360°. Applying the fundamental relations

TRIGONOMETRIC FUNCTIONS OF ANY ANGLE

given in Chapter V, and using the functions of 90° and 180°, verify the functions of 270° and 360° as given in the table.

EXAMPLE

$\sin 270° = \sin (180° + 90°) = \sin 180° \cos 90° + \cos 180° \sin 90°.$
$= (0) \times (0) + (-1) \times (1) = -1.$

Angle	sin	cos	tan	cot
270°	−1	0	∞	0
360°	0	1	0	∞

53. Functions of (90° ± A), when A is acute

Theorem I

In finding the functions of (90° ± A), the names of the functions always change, and the signs may change.

Functions of (90° − A). In the right triangle ACB we have

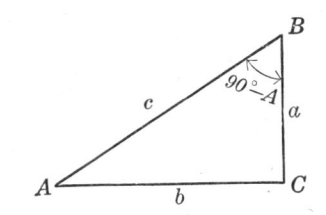

$\sin (90° - A) = \sin B = \cos A.$
$\cos (90° - A) = \cos B = \sin A.$
$\tan (90° - A) = \tan B = \cot A.$
$\cot (90° - A) = \cot B = \tan A.$
$\sec (90° - A) = \sec B = \csc A.$
$\csc (90° - A) = \csc B = \sec A.$

Since A is acute, $(90° - A)$ also is acute. The functions of all first quadrant angles are positive. Observe that the function of an acute angle is equal to the *co-function* of the complementary angle. Thus, $\sin 24° = \cos 66°$, $\cot 60° = \tan 30°$, $\cos 18° = \sin 72°$, and $\tan 75° = \cot 15°$.

Functions of (90° + A). It is evident that $(90° + A)$ is a second quadrant angle. Construct the angle $(90° + A)$ and the angle

A, each angle having its vertex at O. Mark off $OP = OP'$. Let fall perpendiculars CP and $C'P'$ to the initial line. The right triangles OCP and $OC'P'$ are congruent. Why? Hence

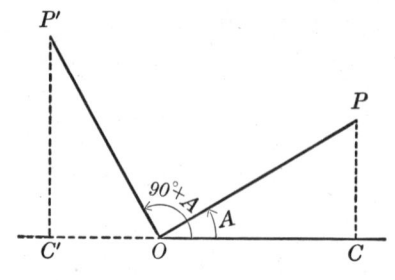

$$\sin(90° + A) = \sin COP' = \frac{C'P'}{OP'} = \frac{OC}{OP} = \cos A.$$

$$\cos(90° + A) = \cos COP' = \frac{OC'}{OP'} = \frac{-CP}{OP} = -\sin A.$$

$$\tan(90° + A) = \tan COP' = \frac{C'P'}{OC'} = \frac{OC}{-CP} = -\cot A.$$

$$\cot(90° + A) = \cot COP' = \frac{OC'}{C'P'} = \frac{-CP}{OC} = -\tan A.$$

To find the function of a second quadrant angle, subtract 90° from the angle and use the co-function, assigning the proper sign.

EXAMPLES

$$\sin 110° = \sin(90° + 20°) = \cos 20°.$$
$$\cos 140° = \cos(90° + 50°) = -\sin 50°.$$
$$\tan 125° = \tan(90° + 35°) = -\cot 35°.$$

See page 100, where the signs of the functions in the four quadrants are given.

54. Functions of (180° ± A), when A is acute

Theorem II

In finding the functions of (180° ± A), the names of the functions never change, but the signs may change.

Functions of (180° − A). See summary, top of page 59.

To find the function of a second quadrant angle, subtract the angle from 180° and use the same function, assigning the proper sign.

TRIGONOMETRIC FUNCTIONS OF ANY ANGLE

EXAMPLES
$\sin 160° = \sin (180° - 20°) = \sin 20°.$
$\cos 115° = \cos (180° - 65°) = - \cos 65°.$
$\tan 142° = \tan (180° - 38°) = - \tan 38°.$

Functions of (180° + A). It is evident that this angle is a third quadrant angle. Construct the angle A and the angle $(180° + A)$. Mark off $OP = OP'$. Let fall perpendiculars CP and $C'P'$ to the initial line and the initial line produced. The right triangles OCP and $OC'P'$ are congruent. Why?

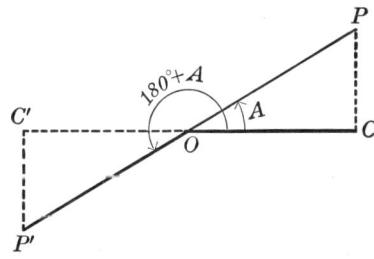

$$\sin (180° + A) = \sin COP' = \frac{C'P'}{OP'} = \frac{-CP}{OP} = - \sin A.$$

$$\cos (180° + A) = \cos COP' = \frac{OC'}{OP'} = \frac{-OC}{OP} = - \cos A.$$

$$\tan (180° + A) = \tan COP' = \frac{C'P'}{OC'} = \frac{-CP}{-OC} = \tan A.$$

To find the functions of a third quadrant angle, subtract 180° from the angle and use the same function, assigning the proper sign.

EXAMPLES
$\sin 200° = \sin (180° + 20°) = - \sin 20°.$
$\cos 220° = \cos (180° + 40°) = - \cos 40°.$
$\tan 250° = \tan (180° + 70°) = \tan 70°.$

If in Theorem I we change 90° to 270° or any *odd multiple of 90°*, the meaning of the theorem is not changed.

If in Theorem II we change 180° to 360° or *any multiple of 180°*, the meaning of the theorem is not changed.

As a result the formulas for functions of 90° ± A, 180° ± A *in terms of functions of A are seen to hold whether or not A is acute.*

The above theorems give us a means of finding the functions of any angle in terms of functions of an acute angle.

EXAMPLES
$\sin 250° = \sin (270° - 20°) = - \cos 20°.$
$\sin 320° = \sin (270° + 50°) = - \cos 50°.$

$$\cos 320° = \cos (360° - 40°) = +\cos 40°.$$
$$\tan 380° = \tan (360° + 20°) = +\tan 20°.$$
$$\sin 550° = \sin (540° + 10°) = -\sin 10°.$$

EXERCISES

Express the following functions in terms of functions of angles less than 45°.

1. sin 165°.
2. cos 130°.
3. sin 215°.
4. cos 250°.
5. tan 110°.
6. cot 200°.
7. sin 285°.
8. cos 290°.
9. sin 340°.
10. tan 305°.
11. cot 265°.
12. sin 375°.
13. cos 400°.
14. tan 600°.
15. sin 820°.

16. Verify the following values of the functions. For example,
$$\sin 210° = \sin (180° + 30°) = -\sin 30° = -\tfrac{1}{2}.$$

Angle	sin	cos	tan	cot
210°	$-\tfrac{1}{2}$	$-\tfrac{\sqrt{3}}{2}$	$\tfrac{1}{\sqrt{3}} = \tfrac{\sqrt{3}}{3}$	$\sqrt{3}$
225°	$-\tfrac{1}{\sqrt{2}} = -\tfrac{\sqrt{2}}{2}$	$-\tfrac{1}{\sqrt{2}} = -\tfrac{\sqrt{2}}{2}$	1	1
240°	$-\tfrac{\sqrt{3}}{2}$	$-\tfrac{1}{2}$	$\sqrt{3}$	$\tfrac{1}{\sqrt{3}} = \tfrac{\sqrt{3}}{3}$
300°	$-\tfrac{\sqrt{3}}{2}$	$\tfrac{1}{2}$	$-\sqrt{3}$	$-\tfrac{1}{\sqrt{3}} = -\tfrac{\sqrt{3}}{3}$
315°	$-\tfrac{1}{\sqrt{2}} = -\tfrac{\sqrt{2}}{2}$	$\tfrac{1}{\sqrt{2}} = \tfrac{\sqrt{2}}{2}$	-1	-1
330°	$-\tfrac{1}{2}$	$\tfrac{\sqrt{3}}{2}$	$-\tfrac{1}{\sqrt{3}} = -\tfrac{\sqrt{3}}{3}$	$-\sqrt{3}$

55. Functions of negative angles

A *negative angle* is formed when the rotating line moves clockwise. In the figures the negative angle is indicated by $-A$. The right triangle DOP is constructed so as to be congruent to the right triangle DOP'.

TRIGONOMETRIC FUNCTIONS OF ANY ANGLE

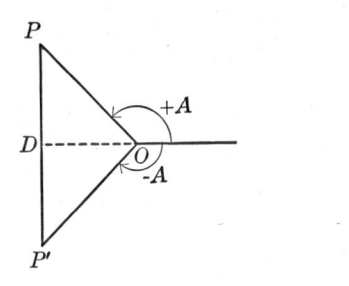

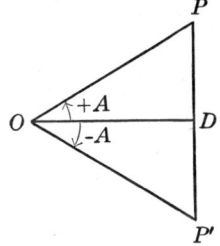

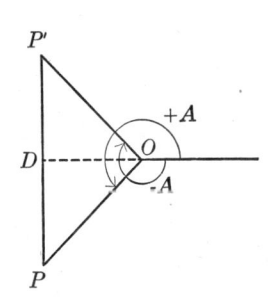

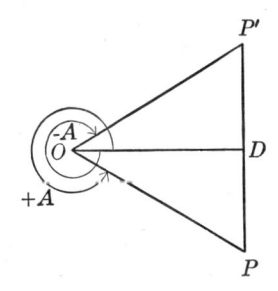

$$\sin(-A) = \frac{DP'}{OP'} = \frac{-DP}{OP} = -\sin A.$$

$$\cos(-A) = \frac{OD}{OP'} = \frac{OD}{OP} = \cos A.$$

$$\tan(-A) = \frac{DP'}{OD} = \frac{-DP}{OD} = -\tan A.$$

$$\cot(-A) = \frac{OD}{DP'} = \frac{OD}{-DP} = -\cot A.$$

EXAMPLES

$\sin(-30°) = -\sin 30° = -\tfrac{1}{2}.$
$\cos(-60°) = \cos 60° = \tfrac{1}{2}.$
$\tan(-45°) = -\tan 45° = -1.$
$\sin(-120°) = -\sin 120° = -\dfrac{\sqrt{3}}{2}.$
$\cos(-225°) = \cos 225° = -\dfrac{1}{\sqrt{2}} = -\dfrac{\sqrt{2}}{2}.$
$\tan(-225°) = -\tan 225° = -1.$

56. Extended proof of the formula for the sine of the sum of two angles

On page 83, Chapter V, it is proved that
$$\sin(A + B) = \sin A \cos B + \cos A \sin B,$$

where $(A + B)$ is acute or obtuse. It remains to be shown that the relation holds for angles of any size.

Assume that A and B are acute angles. Let $A_1 = 90° + A$.
$$\sin(A_1 + B) = \sin[(90° + A) + B].$$
$$\sin[(90° + A) + B] = \sin(90° + A)\cos B + \cos(90° + A)\sin B.$$
$$\sin(A_1 + B) = \cos A \cos B - \sin A \sin B.$$
$$\cos A = \sin(90° + A) = \sin A_1.$$
$$\sin A = -\cos(90° + A) = -\cos A_1.$$
Then $\sin(A_1 + B) = \sin A_1 \cos B + \cos A_1 \sin B.$
Let $A_2 = 180° + A$.
$$\sin(A_2 + B) = \sin[(180° + A) + B].$$
$$\sin[(180° + A) + B] = \sin(180° + A)\cos B + \cos(180° + A)\sin B.$$
$$= -\sin A \cos B - \cos A \sin B.$$
$$\sin A = -(180° + A) = -\sin A_2.$$
$$\cos A = -\cos(180° + A) = -\cos A_2.$$
Then $\sin(A_2 + B) = \sin A_2 \cos B + \cos A_2 \sin B.$

Increasing the acute angle A, or the acute angle B, by multiples of 90°, we find that the sine of the sum of the two angles reduces to the same form as $\sin(A + B)$. Hence we conclude that the original relation is true for angles of any size. The extended proof for the cosine of the sum of two angles is similar. To develop the proof for negative angles we should use $A_1 = A - 90°$ and $A_2 = A - 180°$, etc.

In a like manner we can prove that the relation for the sine and cosine of the difference of two angles is true for angles of any size.

57. Graphs of the trigonometric functions

The nature and variation of the trigonometric functions can be shown by the graphs of the functions. Also their graphs may be used in solving certain kinds of equations.

58. The sine curve

To find the graph of $y = \sin x$.
(1) Assign values to x.
(2) Determine the corresponding values of y.
(3) Take each pair of values of x and y as coördinates of a point and locate the point.
(4) Draw a curve through the points.

TRIGONOMETRIC FUNCTIONS OF ANY ANGLE

Only that part of the graph of $y = sin\ x$ for values of x from 0° to 360° is represented.

x in degrees	x in radians	sin x	y
0°	0	0	0
30°	$\frac{\pi}{6}$	.50	.50
45°	$\frac{\pi}{4}$	.71	.71
60°	$\frac{\pi}{3}$	.87	.87
90°	$\frac{\pi}{2}$	1.00	1.00
120°	$\frac{2}{3}\pi$	.87	.87
135°	$\frac{3}{4}\pi$	.71	.71
150°	$\frac{5}{6}\pi$	.50	.50
180°	π	0	0

The values of $sin\ x$ between 180° and 360° are negative and equal to the sines of the angles between 0° and 180°. Since $sin\ (180° + A) = -sin\ A$, and $sin\ (360° - A) = -sin\ A$, A being acute, it is not necessary to tabulate the sines of the angles between 180° and 360°. Choose a convenient unit on the X-axis to represent π. Then mark off the fractional parts of π as used in the tabulation.

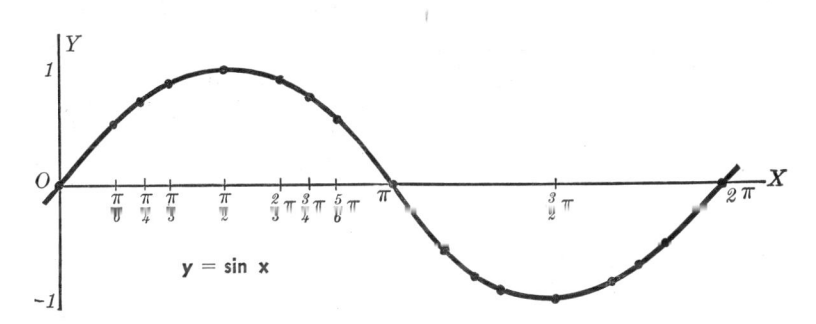

59. The cosine curve

Following the plan for finding the graph of $y = \sin x$, it is easily shown that the graph of $y = \cos x$ appears as shown in the figure.

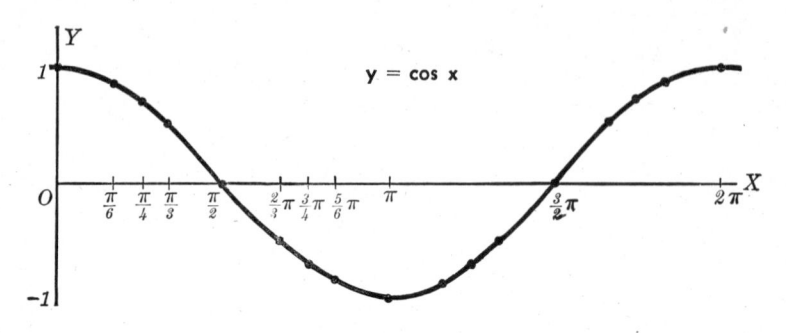

Another way to find the sine curve.
(1) Draw a circle of any radius.
(2) Mark off equal angles at the center.
(3) On a center line mark off a convenient unit to represent π.
(4) Divide this unit into the same number of equal parts as the number of equal angles at the center of the circle.
(5) At each division point construct a line perpendicular to the center line.
(6) From each division point on the circumference of the circle draw a line parallel to the center line to intersect the corresponding perpendicular line.
(7) Mark each point of intersection.
(8) Draw a curve through the intersection points.

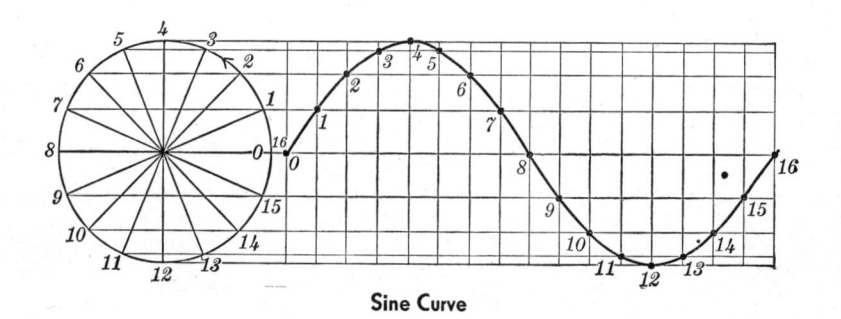

Sine Curve

TRIGONOMETRIC FUNCTIONS OF ANY ANGLE 109

60. The tangent curve

The graph of $y = tan\ x$ has many branches. The breaks in the curve occur when $x = -\frac{3\pi}{2}, -\frac{\pi}{2}, \frac{\pi}{2}, \frac{3\pi}{2}$, etc.

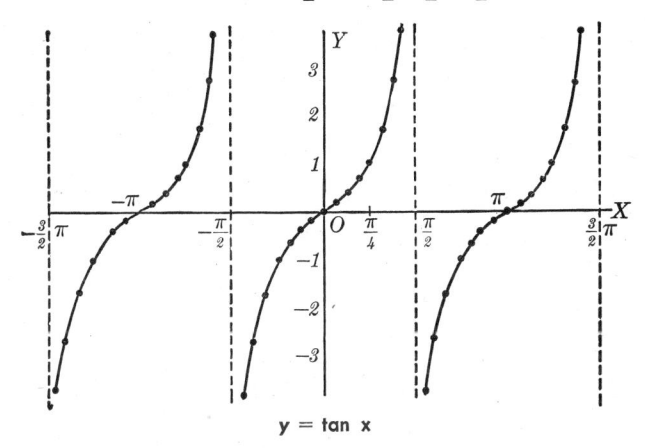

$y = tan\ x$

61. Inverse trigonometric functions

If in the equation $y = sin\ x$ we assign a certain value to x, we know that the value of y is a definite number. If $x = 45°$, $y = .71$. The expression $sin\ x$ expresses a *direct function*.

The inverse problem is to find the values of x, given a value of y.

The question *What is the angle whose sine is $\frac{1}{2}$?* has many answers, namely, $-570°, -210°, 30°, 150°, 390°$, etc. The equation $sin\ x = \frac{1}{2}$ expresses this fact. Symbolically, this fact is expressed by the equation

$$x = sin^{-1}y$$

and is read

x is the angle whose sine is y.

Note: The (-1) is not to be considered as an exponent, but as a symbol to define an angle. The expression $sin^{-1}y$

should be read *the angle whose sine is y*. The smallest angle that satisfies the inverse function is called the *principal value*, or the *primary angle*.

EXERCISES

Read the following, and state the primary angle.

1. $\sin^{-1} \frac{1}{\sqrt{2}}$.
2. $\sin^{-1} 1$.
3. $\cos^{-1} \frac{\sqrt{3}}{2}$.
4. $\tan^{-1} \sqrt{3}$.
5. $\cos^{-1}(-\frac{1}{2})$.
6. $\tan^{-1} 1$.
7. $\cos^{-1} 0$.
8. $\tan^{-1} \frac{1}{\sqrt{3}}$.
9. $\sec^{-1} 2$.

10. What is the value of $\cos(\sin^{-1} \frac{3}{5})$? This means *What is the cosine of the angle whose sine is $\frac{3}{5}$?* Construct the scale triangle for $\sin^{-1} \frac{3}{5}$. Then $\cos(\sin^{-1} \frac{3}{5}) = \frac{4}{5}$. Does $\sin(\sin^{-1} x) = x$? Does $\tan(\tan^{-1} a) = a$?

Find the numerical value of the following, considering only the primary angle.

11. $\cos(\sin^{-1} \frac{4}{5})$.
12. $\tan(\tan^{-1} 1)$.
13. $\sin(\tan^{-1} \frac{1}{2})$.
14. $\tan[\cos^{-1}(-\frac{1}{2})]$.
15. $\sin(\tan^{-1}\sqrt{3})$.
16. $\tan(\sin^{-1} \frac{5}{13})$.
17. $\sin(2 \tan^{-1} \frac{3}{4})$.
18. Show that $\tan^{-1} \frac{1}{2} + \tan^{-1} \frac{1}{3} = \tan^{-1} 1 = 45°$.
Let $\tan^{-1} \frac{1}{2} = A$ and $\tan^{-1} \frac{1}{3} = B$.

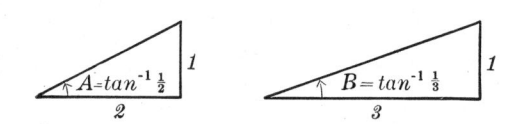

Find the tangent of the sum of the two angles.
$$\tan[\tan^{-1} \tfrac{1}{2} + \tan^{-1} \tfrac{1}{3}] = \tan(A + B).$$
$$\tan(A + B) = \frac{\tan A + \tan B}{1 - \tan A \tan B} = \frac{\frac{1}{2} + \frac{1}{3}}{1 - \frac{1}{2} \times \frac{1}{3}} = 1.$$
Since $\tan(A + B) = 1$, $(A + B) = 45°$. Then
$$\tan^{-1} \tfrac{1}{2} + \tan^{-1} \tfrac{1}{3} = 45°.$$

Verify the following, using only the primary angles.

19. $\tan^{-1} \frac{1}{3} + \tan^{-1} 3 = 90°$. (Remember that any formal expression indicated by a finite number divided by 0 is infinity.)
20. $\tan^{-1} \frac{4}{3} - \tan^{-1} \frac{1}{7} = 45°$.
21. $\tan^{-1} \frac{1}{3} - \tan^{-1} \frac{1}{5} = \tan^{-1} \frac{1}{8}$.
22. $\tan^{-1} a + \tan^{-1} b = \tan^{-1}\left(\frac{a+b}{1-ab}\right)$.

TRIGONOMETRIC FUNCTIONS OF ANY ANGLE 111

23. $2 \tan^{-1} \frac{1}{2} - \sin^{-1} \frac{3}{5} = \cos^{-1} \frac{24}{25}$.
24. $2 \tan^{-1} \frac{1}{2} - \tan^{-1} \frac{1}{7} = 45°$.
25. $\sin^{-1} \frac{3}{5} + \sin^{-1} \frac{8}{17} = \sin^{-1} \frac{77}{85}$.
26. $\tan^{-1} \frac{3}{4} + \tan^{-1} \frac{3}{5} - \tan^{-1} \frac{8}{19} = 45°$.
27. $\tan^{-1} \frac{1}{3} + \tan^{-1} \frac{1}{5} + \tan^{-1} \frac{1}{7} + \tan^{-1} \frac{1}{8} = 45°$.

REVIEW QUESTIONS ON CHAPTER VI

1. Express each of the following in terms of functions of A, where A is acute.

$\sin (90° + A)$. $\sin (180° - A)$. $\sin (180° + A)$.
$\cos (90° + A)$. $\cos (180° - A)$. $\cos (180° + A)$.
$\tan (90° + A)$. $\tan (180° - A)$. $\tan (180° + A)$.

$\sin (270° - A)$. $\sin (270° + A)$. $\sin (360° - A)$.
$\cos (270° - A)$. $\cos (270° + A)$. $\cos (360° - A)$.
$\tan (270° - A)$. $\tan (270° + A)$. $\tan (360° - A)$.

2. Make a table to indicate the sign of each function of an angle in each quadrant.

3. What is meant by a negative angle?

4. Sketch the sine curve for angles from $-180°$ to $360°$.

5. Sketch the cosine curve for the angles from $-180°$ to $360°$.

6. Sketch the tangent curve for the angles from $-180°$ to $360°$.

7. Interpret each of the following expressions.

$\tan^{-1} x$; $\sin^{-1} .2$; $\sin (\cos^{-1} \frac{4}{5})$; $\tan (\sin^{-1} \frac{7}{25})$.

8. Draw a figure to illustrate the last two expressions of exercise 7 and find the primary angle for each.

A Notable Celebration

IN July, 1914, the Royal Society of Edinburgh sponsored an International Congress to commemorate the three-hundredth anniversary of the publication of John Napier's book on Logarithms. Delegates were present from many of the leading universities, academies, learned societies, and corporations of the world.

In addition to a memorial service and a program of scholarly papers, the activities of the Congress included a visit to the ancestral home of Napier, called Merchiston Castle, and an exhibition of Napier relics, books of logarithms, and all kinds of aids to computation. It takes a Memorial Volume of four hundred forty-one pages to record the story of this Napier Tercentenary Celebration.

Sir John Napier was a Scotch nobleman who had mathematics for a hobby. For twenty years he worked at arriving at the idea of logarithms, in developing it, and in making his laborious calculations. Some historians concede to Bürgi, a Swiss, the idea of independent discovery, but said the historian Cajori at the celebration, "The facts as they are known today assign to Napier the glory of a star of the first magnitude as the inventor of logarithms who first gave them to the world."

Napier was the inventor of a system which makes it possible to multiply by adding, to divide by subtracting, to raise to powers by multiplying, and to extract roots by dividing. For this achievement his life and work is indeed worthy of commemoration. Who can estimate the number of years that the use of logarithms has added to the lives of engineers, physicists, actuaries, statisticians, and astronomers? Who can evaluate the great impetus it has given to scientific investigation?

CHAPTER VII

Logarithms and Their Uses

62. Computation using exponents

SINCE the beginning of civilization many devices for saving time and energy in making computations have been invented. The use of exponents gives an easy and quick method of finding products, powers, quotients, and roots of numbers.

Below is given a table of several powers of 2.

Powers of 2		
$2^0 = 1$	$2^6 = 64$	$2^{12} = 4096$
$2^1 = 2$	$2^7 = 128$	$2^{13} = 8192$
$2^2 = 4$	$2^8 = 256$	$2^{14} = 16384$
$2^3 = 8$	$2^9 = 512$	$2^{15} = 32768$
$2^4 = 16$	$2^{10} = 1024$	$2^{16} = 65536$
$2^5 = 32$	$2^{11} = 2048$	$2^{17} = 131072$

EXAMPLES

1. Find 64 × 512.

In the table we see that $64 = 2^6$ and $512 = 2^9$. You know from the law of exponents in multiplication that

$$N^a \times N^b = N^{a+b}.$$

Then $2^6 \times 2^9 = 2^{15}$. In the table we find $2^{15} = 32768$. Then 64 × 512 = 32768.

2. Find $65536 \div 256$.

$65536 \div 256 = 2^{16} \div 2^8$. You know from the law of exponents in division that
$$N^a \div N^b = N^{a-b}.$$
$2^{16} \div 2^8 = 2^8 = 256$. Then $65536 \div 256 = 256$.

3. Find the square of 128.
$128 = 2^7$. You know that
$$(N^a)^b = N^{ab}.$$
$(128)^2 = (2^7)^2 = 2^{14} = 16384$.

4. Find the fourth root of 65536.
$65536 = 2^{16}$. You know that
$$\sqrt[b]{N^a} = N^{\frac{a}{b}}.$$
$\sqrt[4]{65536} = \sqrt[4]{2^{16}} = (2^{16})^{\frac{1}{4}} = 2^4 = 16$.

5. Find $\dfrac{\sqrt[5]{32768} \times (128)^3}{32^2 \times 2048}$.

$\sqrt[5]{32768} = \sqrt[5]{2^{15}} = 2^3$; $128^3 = (2^7)^3 = 2^{21}$; $32^2 = (2^5)^2 = 2^{10}$; $2048 = 2^{11}$. Then
$$\frac{2^3 \times 2^{21}}{2^{10} \times 2^{11}} = \frac{2^{24}}{2^{21}} = 2^3 = 8.$$

EXERCISES

In the following exercises use the table of powers of 2.

1. 8×128.
2. 64×2048.
3. 256×512.
4. 128×16384.
5. $65536 \div 8192$.
6. $1024 \div 16$.
7. $262144 \div 4096$.
8. 16^3.
9. 32^5.
10. 64^3.
11. 4^8.
12. 1024^2.
13. $\sqrt[3]{32768}$.
14. $\sqrt[4]{1048576}$.

15. $\dfrac{256 \times 4096}{128}$.

16. $\dfrac{16384 \times 32768}{512 \times 8192}$.

63. Logarithm of a number

Logarithms are *exponents*. In the expression $2^5 = 32$, the exponent 5 is called a *logarithm*. The number 2 is called the *base*. Any positive number (except 1) may be used as a base. Thus when we say $3^4 = 81$, 3 is the base. Then the

logarithm of 81 to the base 3 is 4.

Since $10^3 = 1000$, we say that the

logarithm of 1000 to the base 10 is 3.

LOGARITHMS AND THEIR USES

In general, for $B^x = N$ we say that the
logarithm of N to the base B is x.

Symbolically, the above expressions are written

$B^x = N$ *(exponential form).*

$x = \log_B N$ *(logarithmic form).*

EXERCISES

Write in the logarithmic form.

1. $5^2 = 25$.
2. $4^3 = 64$.
3. $2^5 = 32$.
4. $8^2 = 64$.

5. $10^3 = 1000$.
6. $5^0 = 1$.
7. $N^0 = 1$.
8. $4^{-2} = \frac{1}{16}$.

9. $8^{\frac{1}{3}} = 2$.
10. $25^{-\frac{1}{2}} = \frac{1}{5}$.
11. $4^{\frac{3}{2}} = 8$.
12. $(-8)^{-\frac{1}{3}} = -\frac{1}{2}$.

Write in the exponential form.

13. $2 = \log_5 25$.
14. $3 = \log_3 27$.

15. $5 = \log_2 32$.
16. $\log_9 81 = 2$.

17. $\log_7 49 = 2$.
18. $\log_2 16 = 4$.

Determine the logarithms.

19. $\log_2 8$.
20. $\log_6 36$.
21. $\log_{10} 1000$.

Common logarithms. Since 10 is the base of our number system, 10 is a convenient base to use in the logarithmic scheme. Logarithms of numbers expressed to the base 10 are called *common logarithms.* The following table should be studied. The base 10 is omitted in the logarithmic form.

Exponential form	*Logarithmic form*
$10^3 = 1000.$	$3 = \log 1000.$
$10^2 = 100.$	$2 = \log 100.$
$10^1 = 10.$	$1 = \log 10.$
$10^0 = 1.$	$0 = \log 1.$
$\frac{1}{10} = 10^{-1} = .1.$	$-1 = \log .1.$
$\frac{1}{10^2} = 10^{-2} = .01.$	$-2 = \log .01.$
$\frac{1}{10^3} = 10^{-3} = .001.$	$-3 = \log .001.$

If $10^x = 3.16$, what is the value of x? Since 3.16 is between 1 and 10, the value of x is between 0 and 1. Hence x is 0 plus a positive decimal fraction, or $x = 0.5 = \frac{1}{2}$. This can be verified by taking the square root of 10. The value of x is .4997 or about .5.

Verify the following.

$10^{\frac{1}{2}} = 10^{.5} = 3.16.$ $10^{\frac{1}{8}} = 10^{.125} = 1.334.$

$10^{\frac{1}{4}} = 10^{.25} = 1.78.$ $10^{\frac{3}{8}} = 10^{.375} = 2.375.$

It is known that $10^{1.6253} = 42.2$. Hence log 42.2 = 1.6253.

Characteristic and mantissa. The logarithm, or exponent, is made up of two parts. The integral part is called the *characteristic*. The fractional part is called the *mantissa*.

Study carefully the following tabulation, where several numbers are expressed as the product of a power of 10 and a number between 1 and 10.

$422 = 100 \times 4.22 = 10^2 \times 4.22 = 10^2 \times 10^{0.6253} = 10^{2.6253}.$

$422 = 10^{2.6253}.$

$42.2 = 10^{1.6253}.$

$4.22 = 10^{0.6253}.$

$.422 = 10^{\bar{1}.6253}.$

$.0422 = 10^{\bar{2}.6253}.$

Observe that the mantissa is the same for each number. The mantissas may be found in the table at the end of the book.

Special scheme for finding characteristics. When using a table to find the logarithm of a number, the student supplies the characteristic.

For an *integer* the characteristic is *positive* and *one less* than the number of figures to the left of the decimal point.

For a *decimal number* the characteristic is *negative* and *one more* than the number of zeros between the decimal point and the first significant figure.

How to find a mantissa in the table. Here is shown a portion of a table of mantissas as given on page 165.

N	0	1	2	3	4	5	6	7	8	9
42	6232	6243	6253	6263	6274	6284	6294	6304	6314	6325
43	6335	6345	6355	6365	6375	6385	6395	6405	6415	6425

In the table, the decimal points are omitted, and the characteristics are to be supplied by the student. In the table, the mantissa of the logarithm of 4.22 is given as .6253. Read down the column

LOGARITHMS AND THEIR USES

headed by N until the number 42 is reached. Then find the mantissa opposite 42 and in the column headed by 2, the third figure of 422.

Show that the log 4.35 is 0.6385.

64. Learning to use logarithms

1. *The logarithm of a product of two or more numbers is equal to the sum of the logarithms of the numbers.*

$$\log AB = \log A + \log B.$$

Proof: Let $A = 10^x$. Then $x = \log A$.
 Let $B = 10^y$. Then $y = \log B$.
$\log AB = \log(10^x \times 10^y) = \log 10^{x+y} = x + y = \log A + \log B.$

EXAMPLE

$\log(24 \times 36) = \log 24 + \log 36.$

2. *The logarithm of a quotient of two numbers is equal to the difference of the logarithms of the numbers.*

$$\log \frac{A}{B} = \log A - \log B.$$

Proof: Let $A = 10^x$. Then $x = \log A$.
 Let $B = 10^y$. Then $y = \log B$.

$$\log \frac{10^x}{10^y} = \log(10^{x-y}) = x - y = \log A - \log B.$$

EXAMPLE

$\log \frac{76}{65} = \log 76 - \log 65.$

3. *The logarithm of an integral power of a number is equal to the exponent of the number times the logarithm of the number.*

$$\log N^x = x \log N.$$

Proof: $N^x = N \times N \times N \times N \times \ldots$ to x factors.
 $\log N^x = \log N + \log N + \log N + \ldots$ to x terms. See 1 above.

$$\log N^x = x \log N.$$

EXAMPLE

$\log 42^5 = 5 \log 42.$

4. *The logarithm of a root of a number is equal to the logarithm of the number divided by the index of the root.*

$$\log \sqrt[n]{N} = \frac{\log N}{n}.$$

Proof: $N = 10^x$. $x = \log N$. Taking the nth root of each member of $N = 10^x$, we get $\sqrt[n]{N} = \sqrt[n]{10^x}$ or $N^{\frac{1}{n}} = 10^{\frac{x}{n}}$.

$$\log N^{\frac{1}{n}} = \frac{x}{n} = \frac{\log N}{n}.$$

EXAMPLE

$\log \sqrt[3]{6^2} = \log 6^{\frac{2}{3}} = \frac{2}{3} \log 6.$

COMPUTATION EXAMPLES

1. $R = \dfrac{35 \times 48}{72}.$

Add: $\log 35 = 1.5441$
$\log 48 = 1.6812$
$ 3.2253$
Subtract: $\log 72 = 1.8573$
$\log R = 1.3680$

Searching the table of mantissas, we find .3680 nearest to .3674 in the column headed by 3. Then go to the left and find 23 in the column headed by N.

Hence $R = 23.3$.

The value of R is expressed to the nearest third figure as found in the tables.

2. $R = \dfrac{(45.8)^{\frac{1}{2}} \times (16)^3}{(2.4)^{\frac{1}{4}}}.$

Adding, $\quad \frac{1}{2} \log 45.8 = 0.8305$
$ 3 \log 16 = 3.6123$
$\phantom{Adding, \quad \frac{1}{2} \log 45.8 =\ } 4.4428$ (log of numerator)
Subtracting, $\frac{1}{4} \log 2.4 = 0.0951$ (log of denominator)
$ \log R = 4.3477$
$ R = 22300$

3. $R = \left[\dfrac{24.6 \times (12.5)^{\frac{2}{5}}}{(8.64)^{\frac{3}{4}}}\right]^{\frac{1}{5}}.$

Adding, $\qquad \log 24.6 = 1.3909$
$ \frac{2}{5} \log 12.5 = 0.4388$
$ 1.8297$
Subtracting, $\frac{3}{4} \log 8.64 = 0.7024$
$ \log K = 1.1273$

(K is the expression within the brackets.)

LOGARITHMS AND THEIR USES

$$\tfrac{1}{5} \log K = 0.2255$$
$$\log R = 0.2255$$
$$R = 1.68$$

Negative characteristics. Since the characteristic of the logarithm of a decimal number is negative, certain difficulties are met when using logarithms in computation. It is customary to change the form of the characteristic as explained in the following examples.

$$\log .128 = -1 + .1072 = \overline{1}.1072 = 9.1072 - 10.$$
$$\log .0128 = -2 + .1072 = \overline{2}.1072 = 8.1072 - 10.$$
$$\log .00128 = -3 + .1072 = \overline{3}.1072 = 7.1072 - 10.$$

In each of the examples we see that 10 has been added to the characteristic and also subtracted. For the first logarithm we have $(-1 + 10) - 10 = 9 - 10$. The value of the logarithm is not changed. When working with negative characteristics, we may add and subtract 10 or any multiple of 10. In the tables, the (-10) is omitted.

Example

Find $\sqrt{.24}$.

$$\log \sqrt{.24} = \log (.24)^{\tfrac{1}{2}} = \tfrac{1}{2} \log .24.$$
$$\log .24 = \overline{1}.3802 = 9.3802 - 10.$$

Before dividing by 2, add 10 and subtract 10. This gives $19.3802 - 20$. The 10 is added and subtracted in order to avoid a characteristic which has (-5) at the end.

$$\tfrac{1}{2} \log .24 = \tfrac{1}{2} (19.3802 - 20) = 9.6901 - 10.$$

Searching the table we find that the mantissa 6901 corresponds to the number 49. Since the characteristic is $(9 - 10)$ or -1, the square root of .24 is .49.

Before dividing a logarithm by an integer, arrange the subtracted part of the characteristic so that after division a (-10) is in the quotient.

EXERCISES

Verify the following.

1. $\log \sqrt{.16} = 9.6021 - 10.$
2. $\log \sqrt{.084} = 9.4622 - 10.$
3. $\log \sqrt[3]{.645^2} = 9.8731 - 10.$

Examples

Verify the following computations. In these examples many of the fundamental principles of logarithms are applied.

1. $R = \sqrt[3]{.128^5}$.

$$\begin{array}{r} 9.1072 - 10 \\ 5 \\ \hline 45.5360 - 50 \\ 20 \quad\quad -20 \\ \hline 3)\,25.5360 - 30 \\ \end{array}$$
$\log R = 8.5120 - 10$
$R = .0325$

2. $R = (.018)^{\frac{3}{2}} \times 8.5$.

$\frac{3}{2} \log .018 = 7.3830 - 10$
$\log 8.5 \ \ = 0.9294$
$\log R \ = \overline{8.3124 - 10}$
$R \ = .0205$

In order that results agree, it is advisable to perform first the multiplication, and then the division. To find $\frac{3}{2} \log N$, multiply $\log N$ by 3 and then divide by 2.

3.
$$R = \sqrt[4]{\left[\frac{(.024)^{\frac{7}{3}} \times (.125)^3}{(.846)^{\frac{1}{2}}}\right]^{\frac{2}{5}}}.$$

$\frac{7}{3} \log .024 = \ \ 6.2205 - 10$
$3 \log .125 = \ \ 7.2907 - 10$
$\quad\quad\quad\quad\quad\ \ \overline{13.5112 - 20}$
$\frac{1}{2} \log .846 = \ \ 9.9637 - 10$
$\quad\quad\quad\quad\quad\ \ \overline{3.5475 - 10}$
$\quad\quad\quad\quad\quad\quad\quad\quad\ \ 2$
$\quad\quad\quad\quad\quad\ \ \overline{7.0950 - 20}$
$\quad\quad\quad\quad\quad\ \ 30 \quad\quad -30$
$\quad\quad\quad\quad 5)\,\overline{37.0950 - 50}$
$\quad\quad\quad\quad\quad\ \ 7.4190 - 10$
$\quad\quad\quad\quad\quad\ \ 30 \quad\quad -30$
$\quad\quad\quad\quad 4)\,\overline{37.4190 - 40}$
$\log R = \ \ 9.3548 - 10$
$R = .226$

EXERCISES

Find answers to nearest three figures before pointing off according to the characteristic.

1. $\dfrac{12.5 \times .62}{.0845}$.

2. $\sqrt[3]{\dfrac{4.63}{.014}}$.

3. $\left[\dfrac{.745}{.025}\right]^{\frac{3}{2}}$.

4. $\sqrt[5]{\dfrac{416 \times .084}{.65}}$.

5. $\dfrac{\sqrt{2} \times \sqrt{3} \times \sqrt{.5}}{\sqrt[3]{.15}}$.

6. $46^{.15} \times .8^{\frac{1}{3}}$.

7. $\sqrt[3]{\left[\dfrac{.85 \times 1.04}{.356 \times .051}\right]^{\frac{4}{5}}}$.

65. Logarithm of a number not specifically given in the table

Find the logarithm of 4863.

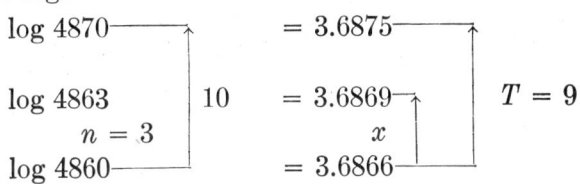

$$\log 4870 = 3.6875$$
$$\log 4863 \quad 10 \quad = 3.6869 \quad T = 9$$
$$n = 3 \qquad\qquad x$$
$$\log 4860 \quad\quad = 3.6866$$

It is not necessary to read the mantissa as a decimal.

We see that a difference of 10 in the number makes a difference of 9 (T) in the tables. A difference of 3 (n) in the number will make what difference (x) in the table? We shall assume that the change in the numbers is proportional to the change in the table. This assumption is not correct, but sufficiently accurate for most computations. A difference of 3 in the number will make a difference of $\frac{3}{10}$ of 9 in the table. $\frac{3}{10}$ of 9 = 2.7. Add 3 to the logarithm of 4860.

For a four-figure number the additive correction is

$$x = \frac{n}{10} \times T.$$

For a five-figure number the additive correction is

$$x = \frac{n}{100} \times T.$$

EXERCISES

Verify the following.
1. log 24.96 = 1.3972.
2. log 354.2 = 2.5492.
3. log .3486 = 9.5423 − 10.
4. log 3.493 = 0.5432.
5. log 846.25 = 2.9275.
6. log .018438 = 8.2657 − 10.

$\frac{6}{10} \times 17 = 10.2$ or 10.
$\frac{2}{10} \times 12 = 2.4$ or 2.
$\frac{6}{10} \times 12 = 7.2$ or 7.
$\frac{3}{10} \times 13 = 3.9$ or 4.
$\frac{25}{100} \times 5 = 1.25$ or 1.
$\frac{38}{100} \times 24 = 9.12$ or 9.

66. How to find a number corresponding to a given logarithm

Given $\log N = 2.4693$; find N.

$$\log 295 \qquad\qquad = 2.4698$$
$$\log N\ (294.67) \quad 1 \quad = 2.4693 \qquad T = 15$$
$$\qquad\qquad\qquad\qquad t = 10$$
$$\log 294 \qquad\qquad = 2.4683$$

If a difference of 15 (T) in the table makes a difference of 1 in the number, then a difference of 10 (t) in the table will make a difference of $\frac{10}{15}$ of 1 in the number. $\frac{10}{15}$ of $1 = .67$.

Annex .67 to 294. A characteristic of 2 means that there are three figures to the left of the decimal point in the number.

Instead of dealing with decimal parts for the differences of the number, it is convenient to think in terms of a three-figure number. In the above example the 67 was annexed to the right of 294 and then pointed off for the characteristic 2.

The annexed part of the number is expressed by $n = \dfrac{t}{T}$.

EXERCISES

Verify the following.

1. $\log N = 2.6382.$ $N = 434.7.$ $\frac{7}{10} = .7.$
2. $\log N = 9.8646 - 10.$ $N = .73217.$ $\frac{1}{6} = .17.$
3. $\log N = 3.1846.$ $N = 1529.655.$ $\frac{28}{29} = .9655.$
4. $\log N = 1.0178.$ $N = 10.419.$ $\frac{8}{42} = .19.$

Note: When negative numbers appear in a computation, the sign of the result is determined by the algebraic law of signs. Make the computation, using the logarithms of all the numbers considered as positive, and then determine the sign of the result.

EXAMPLE

Evaluate $\dfrac{-24 \times 36}{15}$.

The sign of the result is negative.

$$\begin{aligned}
\log 24 &= 1.3802 \\
\log 36 &= 1.5563 \\
& \overline{2.9365} \\
\log 15 &= 1.1761 \\
\log R &= 1.7604 \\
R &= 57.6
\end{aligned}$$

The result is -57.6.

EXERCISES

Evaluate the following.

1. $32.45 \times 16.84.$
2. $\dfrac{248.6}{\sqrt[3]{18.68}}.$
3. $\dfrac{\sqrt{1.565}}{.3468}.$
4. $\dfrac{6.496 \times 2005}{\sqrt[3]{286.4}}.$

LOGARITHMS AND THEIR USES

5. $\dfrac{-4.63 \times 1.824^2}{.08627}$.

6. Show that
$$\sqrt{\dfrac{1.74 \times 24.6^{\frac{3}{4}}}{.052}} = 16.82.$$

7. Show that
$$\sqrt[3]{\dfrac{2.846^{\frac{1}{2}} \times 3.445^2}{.846^{\frac{1}{3}}}} = 2.766.$$

8. Find the radius of a sphere having a volume of 100 cubic inches. The formula to be used is $V = \frac{4}{3}\pi R^3$. Then
$$R = \sqrt[3]{\dfrac{3V}{4\pi}}. \quad \text{Use } \pi = 3.14.$$

9. A man invests $3600 at 5% interest, compounded annually, for a period of 10 years. Find the amount. The formula to be used is $A = P(1 + r)^n$.

10. How much money placed at 5% interest, compounded semi-annually, will accumulate to $1000 at the end of 10 years? *Hint:* In 10 years there are 20 interest periods, at a rate of $2\frac{1}{2}$% per period. Use the formula $P = \dfrac{A}{(1+r)^n}$.

67. Exponential equations

In many types of equations the unknown appears as an exponent. Sometimes the value of the unknown can be determined by inspection, but generally the use of logarithms is required. In the equation $3^x = 81$ the value of x is known to be 4. In the equation $3^x = 20$ the use of logarithms gives an easy method for finding the value of x.

EXAMPLE

Solve the equation $3^x = 20$. The value of x is between 2 and 3.
$$\log(3^x) = \log 20.$$
$$x \log 3 = \log 20.$$
$$x = \dfrac{\log 20}{\log 3} = \dfrac{1.3010}{0.4771} = 2.73.$$

EXERCISES

Solve these equations.

1. $5^x = 625$.
2. $8^x = 512$.
3. $10^x = 7?$
4. $(1.05)^x = 500$.
5. $(2.5)^{-x} = 50$.
6. $x^{2.5} = 18$.

7. In how many years will $1000 at 6% interest amount to $2000, if the interest is compounded annually? *Hint:* The formula to be used is $A = P(1+r)^n$; then $2000 = 1000(1.06)^n$.

8. A man borrowed $2000, agreeing to pay $200 annually, the payment to include the interest at 6%. How many years would it take him to pay off the debt? *Hint:* The formula to be used is

$$(1 + r)^n = \frac{p}{p - Pr}. \text{ Then } n = \frac{\log p - \log (p - Pr)}{\log (1 + r)}.$$

68. How to find logarithms of trigonometric functions

1. Find   log sin 18° 20′.
See table, page 167.

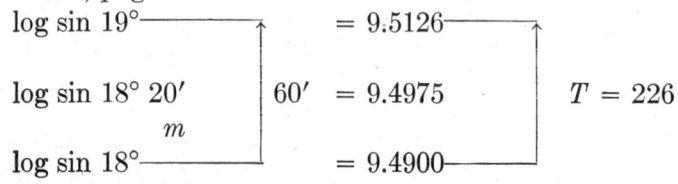

log sin 19°─────────┐   = 9.5126─────────┐

log sin 18° 20′   │ 60′ = 9.4975   │ $T = 226$
          m

log sin 18°───────┘   = 9.4900─────────┘

In computation, the (− 10) should be written.

If 60′ make a difference of 226 in the table, then 20′ will make a difference of $\frac{20}{60}$ of 226 in the table. $\frac{20}{60}$ of 226 = 75. Add 75 to 4900.

If m represents the number of minutes for which interpolation is made, then the correction is

$$\frac{m}{60} \times T.$$

The same method is used in finding the "log tan."

EXERCISES

Verify the following logarithms.

The student should observe that the lower logarithm is the first logarithm met when *reading up (or down)* the sine (or tangent) column. Also by this scheme of tabulation the interpolation correction is *added*.

1. log sin 25° 20′ = 9.6312. $\frac{20}{60}$ of 159 = 53.
2. log sin 35° 43′ = 9.7662. $\frac{43}{60}$ of 106 = 76.
3. log sin 48° 28′ = 9.8742. $\frac{28}{60}$ of 67 = 31.
4. log sin 62° 45′ = 9.9489. $\frac{45}{60}$ of 40 = 30.
5. log sin 4° 50′ = 8.9242. $\frac{50}{60}$ of 967 = 806.
6. log tan 18° 12′ = 9.5168. $\frac{12}{60}$ of 252 = 50.
7. log tan 48° 18′ = 0.0502. $\frac{18}{60}$ of 152 = 46.
8. log tan 4° 45′ = 8.9177. $\frac{45}{60}$ of 974 = 731.
9. log tan 82° 11′ = 0.8630. $\frac{11}{60}$ of 587 = 108.

LOGARITHMS AND THEIR USES

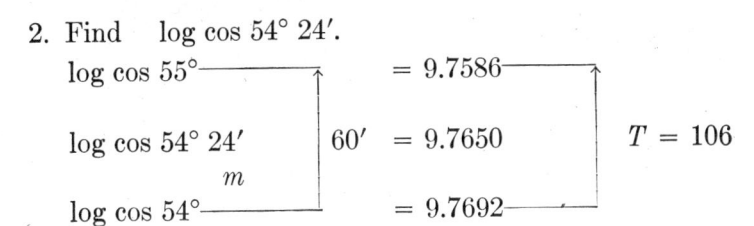

2. Find log cos 54° 24'.

log cos 55° ————————┐   = 9.7586 ————————┐
                    │   │
log cos 54° 24'   │ 60' = 9.7650   │ $T = 106$
          } m │   │
log cos 54° ————————┘   = 9.7692 ————————┘

Note: The lower logarithm is the *first* logarithm met when reading up (or down) the cosine column.

If 60' make a difference of 106 in the table, then 24' will make a difference of $\frac{24}{60}$ of 106 in the table. $\frac{24}{60}$ of 106 = 42. *Subtract* 42 from 7692. The *subtraction correction* is expressed by

$$\frac{m}{60} \times T.$$

The same method is used in finding "log cot."

EXERCISES

Verify the following.

1. log cos 22° 15' = 9.9664.
2. log cos 55° 16' = 9.7557.
3. log cos 6° 48' = 9.9970.
4. log cos 87° 22' = 8.6543.
5. log cot 14° 48' = 0.5782.
6. log cot 53° 14' = 9.8734.
7. log cot 4° 18' = 1.1262.
8. log cot 63° 55' = 9.6898.

$\frac{15}{60}$ of 32 = 8; *subtract*.
$\frac{16}{60}$ of 110 = 29; *subtract*.
$\frac{48}{60}$ of 8 = 6; *subtract*.
$\frac{22}{60}$ of 1760 = 645; *subtract*.
$\frac{48}{60}$ of 313 = 250; *subtract*.
$\frac{14}{60}$ of 158 = 37; *subtract*.
$\frac{18}{60}$ of 974 = 292; *subtract*.
$\frac{55}{60}$ of 190 = 174; *subtract*.

69. How to find the angle corresponding to a given logarithm of a function

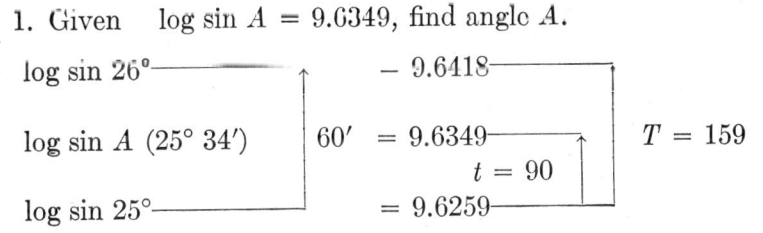

1. Given log sin A = 9.6349, find angle A.

log sin 26° ————————┐   − 9.6418 ————————┐
                    │   │
log sin A (25° 34')│ 60' = 9.6349 ——┐   │ $T = 159$
                    │ $t = 90$ │   │
log sin 25° ————————┘   = 9.6259 ————┴————┘

If a difference of 159 in the table makes a difference of 60' in the angle, then a difference of 90 will make a difference of $\frac{90}{159}$ of 60' in the angle. $\frac{90}{159}$ of 60' = 34'. Add 34' to 25°.

The correction of the angle in minutes is expressed by

$$\frac{t}{T} \times 60'.$$

The same method is used in finding the angle from "log tan."

EXERCISES
Verify the following.
1. $\log \sin A = 9.4634.$ $A = 16° 54'.$ $\frac{231}{256}$ of $60' = 54'.$
2. $\log \sin A = 9.9517.$ $A = 63° 28'.$ $\frac{18}{38}$ of $60' = 28'.$
3. $\log \sin A = 8.9000.$ $A = 4° 35'.$ $\frac{564}{967}$ of $60' = 35'.$
4. $\log \tan A = 9.0500.$ $A = 6° 25'.$ $\frac{284}{675}$ of $60' = 25'.$
5. $\log \tan A = 0.4694.$ $A = 71° 15'.$ $\frac{64}{252}$ of $60' = 15'.$
6. $\log \tan A = 8.9680.$ $A = 5° 20'.$ $\frac{260}{796}$ of $60' = 20'.$

2. Given $\log \cos A = 9.9774$, find angle A.

$\log \cos 19°$ ——————————————— $= 9.9757$ ———————————

$\log \cos A\ (18°\ 19')$ $60' = 9.9774$ ———— $T = 25$
$t = 8$
$\log \cos 18°$ ——————————————— $= 9.9782$ ———————

Note: The lower logarithm is the first logarithm met as you read down (or up) the cosine column.

If a difference of 25 in the table makes a difference of 60' in the angle, a difference of 8 will make a difference of $\frac{8}{25}$ of 60' in the angle. $\frac{8}{25}$ of $60' = 19'$. Add 19' to 18°.

The additive correction for the angle is expressed by

$$\frac{t}{T} \times 60'.$$

The same method is used in finding the angle from "log cot."

EXERCISES
Verify the following.
1. $\log \cos A = 9.7847.$ $A = 52° 28'.$ $\frac{46}{98}$ of $60' = 28'.$
2. $\log \cos A = 9.8741.$ $A = 41° 33'.$ $\frac{37}{67}$ of $60' = 33'.$
3. $\log \cos A = 9.6664.$ $A = 62° 21'.$ $\frac{52}{146}$ of $60' = 21'.$
4. $\log \cos A = 8.9236.$ $A = 85° 10'.$ $\frac{167}{967}$ of $60' = 10'.$
5. $\log \cot A = 9.6123.$ $A = 67° 44'.$ $\frac{156}{215}$ of $60' = 44'.$
6. $\log \cot A = 0.4824.$ $A = 18° 14'.$ $\frac{58}{252}$ of $60' = 14'.$
7. $\log \cot A = 9.8882.$ $A = 52° 18'.$ $\frac{46}{157}$ of $60' = 18'.$
8. $\log \cot A = 8.8998.$ $A = 85° 26'.$ $\frac{422}{974}$ of $60' = 26'.$

LOGARITHMS AND THEIR USES

REVIEW QUESTIONS ON CHAPTER VII

1. What is a logarithm?
2. Express in logarithmic form: $2^4 = 16$; $3^x = 243$; $x^4 = 625$; $a^x = b$.
3. Express in exponential form: $2 = \log_3 9$; $x = \log_3 81$; $a = \log_c b$; $3 = \log_{10} 1000$.
4. Find the logarithm of each number: 387.2; 9.57; .0346; 98.42; .004825.
5. Find the numbers whose logarithms are: 2.8500; $9.2718 - 10$; 0.5811; $8.5419 - 10$.
6. Use logarithms to evaluate $\sqrt{\dfrac{23.56 \times .7^5}{.084}}$.
7. What is the value of x in
   (a) $10^x = 947$.   (b) $x^7 = 128$.
8. Find the logarithms of the following functions:
   sin 27° 40'.   cos 15° 20'.
   sin 50° 25'.   cos 52° 14'.
   tan 40° 18'.   cot 37° 44'.
   tan 67° 15'.   cot 85° 27'.
9. Find the angles corresponding to the following logarithms:
   log sin $A = 9.7224 - 10$.   log cos $A = 9.9650 - 10$.
   log sin $A = 9.1330 - 10$.   log cos $A = 9.8000 - 10$.
   log tan $A = 9.2836 - 10$.   log cot $A = 0.7245$.
   log tan $A = 0.3120$.   log cot $A = 9.9137 - 10$.

Logarithmic Tables

IN this chapter the solution of the general triangle by logarithms is emphasized. This method of computation calls for the use of tables.

In the system worked out by the Scotch nobleman Napier, the inventor of logarithms, the logarithm of 10^7 was zero. The year following the publication of Napier's work in 1614, his friend Henry Briggs, the English mathematician, went to Edinburgh to discuss with him the desirability of making certain changes in his system.

As the result of the discussion, Briggs made zero the logarithm of unity, and adopted ten as a base. In 1624, Briggs published a table of logarithms from 1 to 20,000, and from 90,000 to 100,000 to the equivalent of 14 decimal places. DeDecker and Vlacq filled in the gap several years later.

The preparation of a monumental new set of tables was inspired by the Napier Tercentenary Celebration. It is the *Logarithmetica Britannica; Being a Standard Table of Logarithms to Twenty Decimal Places*, by A. J. Thompson, Cambridge, England. It will contain the logarithms of numbers from 10,000 to 100,000 and is being published in ten parts. The first part appeared in 1924, and the entire work is now virtually completed.

The text you are studying contains a table of logarithms of numbers from 1 to 1,000 to four decimal places. The use of such a table gives results sufficiently accurate for the purposes of this course. This text also contains a table of logarithms of numbers from 1 to 1,000 to five decimal places for those who desire more accurate results.

CHAPTER

VIII

Solving Triangles by the Use of Logarithms

IN Chapters III and IV solutions of triangles, using the natural functions of angles and the fundamental processes of arithmetic, have been studied. In solving many triangles, however, it is much more convenient and practical to use logarithms in making the computations.

In this chapter, special forms of tabulation are used. The various cases should be studied carefully and all sides and angles verified in order to obtain efficiency and accuracy.

In plane geometry, you have learned that every triangle has six primary elements, three sides and three angles. If any three of these elements, at least one element being a side, are given, it is possible to construct the triangle and find by computation the remaining elements. Also we will use three other secondary elements of a triangle, which can be found in terms of the sides and angles. The secondary elements are (1) the radius of the inscribed circle, (2) the radius of the circumscribed circle, and (3) the area.

Four main cases arise in the solution of the general triangle, which may be classified as follows:

I. Given a side and two angles.
   Use sine theorem.

II. Given two sides and an angle opposite one of the sides.
   Use sine theorem.

III. *Given two sides and the included angle.*
  Use tangent theorem for logarithmic computation. Use cosine theorem for arithmetical computation.
IV. *Given three sides.*
  Use tangent half-angle theorem for logarithmic computation. Use cosine theorem for arithmetical computation.

70. Suggestions for a plan of solution

1. In any triangle $A + B + C = 180°$.
2. Write the given data.
3. Make a scale drawing which is to be used as a check.
4. Write the formulas needed for computation.
5. Make a computational check.
6. Find numbers to the nearest second decimal figure, unless otherwise specified.
7. Find angles to the nearest minute, unless otherwise specified.
8. When necessary, find the value of s to the nearest third decimal figure; s means $\frac{1}{2}(a + b + c)$. This insures greater accuracy in making the computational check.

Check formulas. It is necessary that the student check his final computation. It is better to use formulas that contain as many of the primary elements as possible.

Use the following formula to check Cases I, III, and IV.
$$\frac{a - b}{c} = \frac{\sin \frac{1}{2}(A - B)}{\cos \frac{1}{2} C}.$$
In computation this formula is written
$(a - b) \cos \frac{1}{2} C = c \sin \frac{1}{2}(A - B).$

Development of the above formula. In the figure, for the triangle AEB we have
$$\frac{a - b}{c} = \frac{\sin \frac{1}{2}(A - B)}{\sin \angle AEB}.$$
See page 67 for the construction of this figure.
  $\angle AEB = \frac{1}{2}(A + B) + C.$ Why?
Since $\quad A + B = 180° - C$, then
  $\frac{1}{2}(A + B) = 90° - \frac{1}{2} C.$
  Also $\angle AEB = 90° + \frac{1}{2} C.$

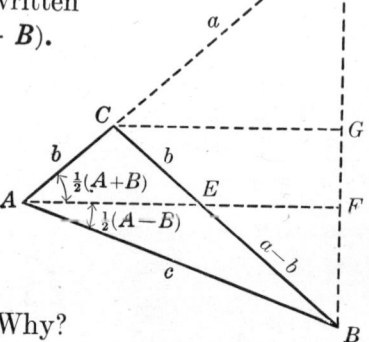

SOLVING TRIANGLES BY THE USE OF LOGARITHMS

$\sin(90° + \frac{1}{2}C) = \cos\frac{1}{2}C$. Why?
Then $\sin \angle AEB = \cos\frac{1}{2}C$.

Substituting this value of sin $\angle AEB$ in the above proportion, we obtain the result.

Use the following formulas to check Case II.
  (1) $a = b \cos C + c \cos B$.
  (2) $b = c \cos A + a \cos C$.
  (3) $c = b \cos A + a \cos B$.

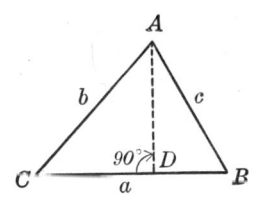

Development of formula (1). In the triangle ABC, $CD = b \cos C$, and $DB = c \cos B$. Also $a = CB = CD + DB$. Hence, $a = b \cos C + c \cos B$. Interchanging the letters, we obtain the formulas (2) and (3).

71. Case I

Given one side and two angles.

EXAMPLE

Given $a = 12$, $A = 64°$, $B = 36°$, to find C, b, c, K, r, and R.

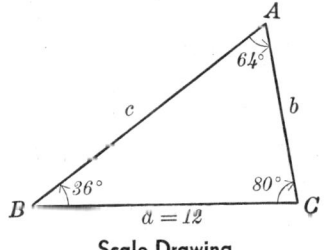

Scale Drawing

Formulas:

$C = 180° - (A + B)$.

$b = \dfrac{a \sin B}{\sin A}$.

$c = \dfrac{a \sin C}{\sin A}$.

$K = \dfrac{a^2 \sin B \sin C}{2 \sin A}$.

$r = \dfrac{K}{s}$.

$R = \dfrac{a}{2 \sin A}$.

Computation:
$C = 180° - (64° + 36°)$.

$\log a =$	1.0792	$\log a =$	1.0792
$\log \sin B =$	$9.7692 - 10$	$\log \sin C =$	$9.9934 - 10$
	$10.8484 - 10$		$11.0726 - 10$
$\log \sin A =$	$9.9537 - 10$	$\log \sin A =$	$9.9537 - 10$
$\log b =$	0.8947	$\log c =$	1.1189
$b =$	7.85	$c =$	13.15

Before attempting to find K, r, and R, it is a good policy to check the values found for C, b, and c.

Check:
$$(a - b) \cos \tfrac{1}{2} C = c \sin \tfrac{1}{2} (A - B).$$

$\log (a - b) =$	$10.6180 - 10$	$\log \sin \tfrac{1}{2}(A - B) =$	$9.3837 - 10$
$\log \cos \tfrac{1}{2} C =$	$9.8843 - 10$	$\log c =$	1.1189
	0.5023		0.5026

In the check it is not necessary to find the numbers corresponding to the logarithms. A close agreement of the logarithms is expected.

$\log a =$	1.0792	$s = \tfrac{1}{2}(a + b + c) =$	16.5
	2	$\log K =$	1.6663
$\log a^2 =$	2.1584	$\log s =$	1.2175
$\log \sin B =$	$9.7692 - 10$	$\log r =$	0.4488
$\log \sin C =$	$9.9934 - 10$	$r =$	2.81
	$21.9210 - 20$	$\log a =$	1.0792
$\log (2 \sin A) =$	$10.2547 - 10$	$\log (2 \sin A) =$	0.2547
$\log K =$	1.6663	$\log R =$	0.8245
$K =$	46.38	$R =$	6.68

The following tabulation form is recommended.

Data and Results			Logarithms	
Given:	a	12	$\log a$	1.0792
	A	64°	$\log b$	0.8947
	B	36°	$\log c$	1.1189
			$\log s$	1.2175
Required:	C	80°	$\log \sin A$	$9.9537 - 10$
	b	7.85	$\log \sin B$	$9.7692 - 10$
	c	13.15	$\log \sin C$	$9.9934 - 10$
	s	16.5	$\log K$	1.6663
	K	46.38	$\log r$	0.4488
	r	2.81	$\log R$	0.8245
	R	6.68	$\log 2$	0.3010

SOLVING TRIANGLES BY THE USE OF LOGARITHMS

EXERCISE

Formulas:

$$C = 180° - (A + B).$$

$$b = \frac{a \sin B}{\sin A}.$$

$$c = \frac{a \sin C}{\sin A}.$$

$$K = \frac{a^2 \sin B \sin C}{2 \sin A}.$$

$$r = \frac{K}{s}.$$

$$R = \frac{a}{2 \sin A}.$$

Data and Results			Logarithms	
Given:	a	10	$\log a$	
	A	60° 26′	$\log b$	
	B	20° 15′	$\log c$	
			$\log s$	
Required:	C		$\log \sin A$	
	b		$\log \sin B$	
	c		$\log \sin C$	
	s		$\log K$	
	K		$\log r$	
	r		$\log R$	
	R		$\log 2$	.3010

Check:

$$(a - b) \cos \tfrac{1}{2} C = c \sin \tfrac{1}{2} (A - B).$$

$\log (a - b) =$ $\log c =$

$\log \cos \tfrac{1}{2} C =$ _____ $\log \sin \tfrac{1}{2} (A - B) =$ _____

72. Case II

Given two sides and an angle opposite one of the sides.

A general discussion of this case is necessary before an example is considered. Since no relation is given concerning the size of either side or the size of the angle, a consideration of the possible constructions is desirable. The constructions are made first when the angle is acute, and secondly when the angle is obtuse.

Let sides a and b and the angle A be the given parts.

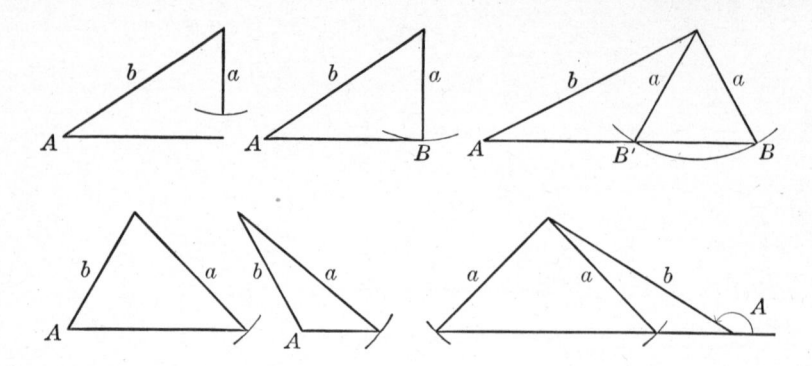

No solution. When $A < 90°$, $a < b \sin A$.

If A is less than 90° and the value of a is less than $(b \sin A)$, no solution is possible.

One solution. When $A < 90°$, $a = b \sin A$.

If A is less than 90° and the value of a is equal to $(b \sin A)$, the solution is a right triangle.

Two solutions. When $A < 90°$, $b > a$, $a > b \sin A$.

If A is less than 90°, the value of a greater than $(b \sin A)$, and b greater than a, two solutions exist.

One solution. When $A < 90°$, $a > b$.

If A is less than 90° and the value of a is greater than b, one solution exists.

One solution. When $A > 90°$, $a > b$.

If A is greater than 90° and the value of a is greater than b, one solution exists.

No solution. When $A > 90°$, $a = b$, or $a < b$.

If A is greater than 90° and the value of a is equal to, or less than, b, no solution exists.

In Case II it is evident that the first derived part is obtained by the use of the *sine theorem*, that is, $\sin B = \dfrac{b \sin A}{a}$. In this formula an ambiguity appears, since the sines of supplementary angles are equal, and the sign of the sine function is positive for all angles between 0° and 180°.

SOLVING TRIANGLES BY THE USE OF LOGARITHMS

EXAMPLE

Given $a = 12$, $b = 18$, $A = 32°$, to find B, B', C, C', c, and c'.

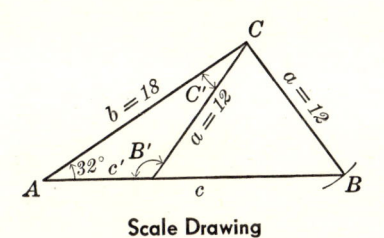

Scale Drawing

Formulas:

$$\sin B = \frac{b \sin A}{a}.$$
$$B' = 180° - B.$$
$$C = 180° - (A + B).$$
$$C' = 180° - (A + B').$$

$$c = \frac{a \sin C}{\sin A}.$$
$$c' = \frac{a \sin C'}{\sin A}.$$

Computation:

$$\begin{aligned}
\log\ b &= 1.2553 \\
\log \sin A &= 9.7242 - 10 \\
\hline
&10.9795 - 10 \\
\log\ a &= 1.0792 \\
\hline
\log \sin B &= 9.9003 - 10 \\
B &= 52° 39' \\
\log\ a &= 1.0792 \\
\log \sin C &= 9.9981 - 10 \\
\hline
&11.0773 - 10 \\
\log \sin A &= 9.7242 - 10 \\
\hline
\log\ c &= 1.3531 \\
c &= 22.55
\end{aligned}$$

$$\begin{aligned}
B' &= \angle CB'A. \\
B' &= 180° - 52° 39'. \\
B' &= 127° 21'. \\
C &= 95° 21'. \\
C' &= 20° 39'. \\
\log\ a &= 1.0792 \\
\log \sin C' &= 9.5472 - 10 \\
\hline
&10.6264 - 10 \\
\log \sin A &= 9.7242 - 10 \\
\hline
\log\ c' &= 0.9022 \\
c' &= 7.98
\end{aligned}$$

Check:

$$c = b \cos A + a \cos B.$$
$$c' = b \cos A + a \cos B'.$$

$22.55 = 15.26 + 7.28$ (approximately).
$7.98 = 15.26 - 7.28.$

The following tabulation scheme is recommended for recording the results of Case II.

Data and Results			Logarithms	
Given:	a	12	$\log a$	1.0792
	b	18	$\log b$	1.2553
	A	32°	$\log c$	1.3531
			$\log c'$	0.9022
Required:	B	52° 39'	$\log \sin A$	9.7242 − 10
	B'	127° 21'	$\log \sin B$	9.9003 − 10
	C	95° 21'	$\log \sin B'$	9.9003 − 10
	C'	20° 39'	$\log \sin C$	9.9981 − 10
	c	22.55	$\log \sin C'$	9.5472 − 10
	c'	7.98		

EXERCISE

Formulas:
Test for number of possible solutions.

$$\sin B = \frac{b \sin A}{a}.$$
$$B' = 180° - B.$$
$$\sin B' = \sin B.$$
$$C = 180° - (A + B).$$
$$C' = 180° - (A + B').$$

$$c = \frac{a \sin C}{\sin A}.$$
$$c' = \frac{a \sin C'}{\sin A}.$$

Data and Results			Logarithms	
Given:	a	27.5	$\log a$	
	b	35	$\log b$	
	A	31° 30'	$\log c$	
			$\log c'$	
Required:	B		$\log \sin A$	
	B'		$\log \sin B$	
	C		$\log \sin B'$	
	C'		$\log \sin C$	
	c		$\log \sin C'$	
	c'			

Check:
$$c = b \cos A + a \cos B.$$
$$c' = b \cos A + a \cos B'.$$

SOLVING TRIANGLES BY THE USE OF LOGARITHMS

73. Case III

Given two sides and the included angle.

EXAMPLE

Given $a = 20$, $b = 10$, $C = 40°$, to find A, B, c, K, r, and R.

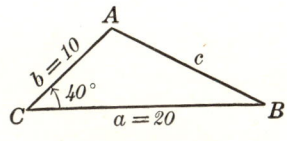

Scale Drawing

Formulas:

$$\tfrac{1}{2}(A + B) = \tfrac{1}{2}(180 - C).$$

$$\tan \tfrac{1}{2}(A - B) = \frac{a - b}{a + b} \tan \tfrac{1}{2}(A + B).$$

$$c = \frac{a \sin C}{\sin A}. \qquad K = \tfrac{1}{2} ab \sin C.$$

$$r = \frac{K}{s}. \qquad R = \frac{c}{2 \sin C}.$$

Computation:

$\tfrac{1}{2}(A + B) = 70°.$
$a + b = 30; \ a - b = 10.$

$\log (a - b) =$	$11.0000 - 10$
$\log (a + b) =$	1.4771
	$9.5229 - 10$
$\log \tan \tfrac{1}{2}(A + B) =$	0.4389
$\log \tan \tfrac{1}{2}(A - B) =$	$9.9618 - 10$
$\tfrac{1}{2}(A - B) =$	$42° \ 29'$
$\tfrac{1}{2}(A + B) =$	$70°$
$A =$	$112° \ 29'$
$B =$	$27° \ 31'$

$\log a =$	1.3010
$\log \sin C =$	$9.8081 - 10$
	$11.1091 - 10$
$\log \sin A =$	$9.9657 - 10$
$\log c =$	1.1434
$c =$	13.91

Check:

$$(a - b) \cos \tfrac{1}{2} C = c \sin \tfrac{1}{2}(A - B).$$

$\log (a - b) =$	$11.0000 - 10$		$\log \sin \tfrac{1}{2}(A - B) =$	$9.8295 - 10$
$\log \cos \tfrac{1}{2} C =$	$9.9730 - 10$		$\log c =$	1.1434
	$20.9730 - 20$			$10.9729 - 10$

See Case I for the forms of computing K, r, and R.

The following tabulation scheme is recommended for recording the results of Case III.

PLANE TRIGONOMETRY

Data and Results			Logarithms	
Given:	a	20	$\log(a-b)$	1.0000
	b	10	$\log(a+b)$	1.4771
	C	40°	$\log \tan \dfrac{A+B}{2}$	0.4389
Required:			$\log \tan \dfrac{A-B}{2}$	9.9618 − 10
	$a-b$	10		
	$a+b$	30	$\log \sin A$	9.9657 − 10
	$\frac{1}{2}(A+B)$	70°	$\log \sin C$	9.8081 − 10
	$\frac{1}{2}(A-B)$	42° 29′	$\log a$	1.3010
	A	112° 29′	$\log b$	1.0000
	B	27° 31′	$\log c$	1.1434
	c	13.91	$\log s$	1.3415
	s	21.955	$\log K$	1.8081
	K	64.29	$\log r$	0.4666
	r	2.93	$\log R$	1.0343
	R	10.82	$\log 2$	0.3010

EXERCISE

Formulas:

$$\tan \frac{A-B}{2} = \frac{a-b}{a+b} \tan \frac{A+B}{2}. \qquad K = \tfrac{1}{2} ab \sin C. \qquad r = \frac{K}{s}.$$

$$c = \frac{a \sin C}{\sin A}. \qquad R = \frac{c}{2 \sin C}.$$

Data and Results			Logarithms	
Given:	a	16	$\log(a-b)$	
	b	11	$\log(a+b)$	
	C	48°	$\log \tan \dfrac{A+B}{2}$	
Required:			$\log \tan \dfrac{A-B}{2}$	
	$a-b$		$\log \sin A$	
	$a+b$		$\log \sin C$	
	$\frac{1}{2}(A+B)$		$\log a$	
	$\frac{1}{2}(A-B)$		$\log b$	
	A		$\log c$	
	B		$\log s$	
	c		$\log K$	
	s		$\log r$	
	K		$\log R$	
	r		$\log 2$	0.3010
	R			

SOLVING TRIANGLES BY THE USE OF LOGARITHMS

$\log (a - b) =$
$\log \cos \frac{1}{2} C =$ _____

Check:
$(a - b) \cos \frac{1}{2} C = c \sin \frac{1}{2} (A - B).$
$\log \sin \frac{1}{2} (A - B) =$
$\log c =$ _____

74. Case IV

Given three sides.

EXAMPLE

Given $a = 12, b = 5, c = 13$, to find A, B, C, K, r, and R.

Formulas:

$$r = \sqrt{\frac{(s - a)(s - b)(s - c)}{s}}.$$

$\tan \frac{1}{2} A = \dfrac{r}{s - a}.$

$\tan \frac{1}{2} B = \dfrac{r}{s - b}.$

$\tan \frac{1}{2} C = \dfrac{r}{s - c}.$

$K = rs.$

$R = \dfrac{abc}{4K}.$

Scale Drawing ($c = 13$, $b = 5$, $a = 12$)

Computation:
$2s = 30; \; s = 15; \; s - a = 3;$
$s - b = 10; \; s - c = 2.$

$\log (s - a) = 0.4771$
$\log (s - b) = 1.0000$
$\log (s - c) = 0.3010$
$ \overline{1.7781}$
$\log s = 1.1761$
$\log r^2 = 0.6020$
$\log r = 0.3010$
$r = 2$

$\log r = 0.3010$
$\log s = 1.1761$
$\log K = \overline{1.4771}$
$K = 30$

$\log (abc) = 2.8921$
$\log (4K) = 2.0792$
$\log R = \overline{0.8129}$
$R = 6.5$

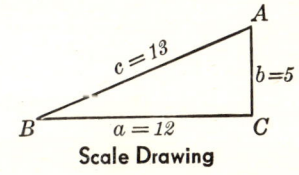

Find half-angles to nearest tenth of a minute.

$\log r = 10.3010 - 10$
$\log (s - a) = \underline{0.4771}$
$\log \tan \frac{1}{2} A = 9.8239 - 10$
$\frac{1}{2} A = 33° 41.5'$
$A = 67° 23'$

$\log r = 10.3010 - 10$
$\log (s - b) = \underline{1.0000}$
$\log \tan \frac{1}{2} B = 9.3010 - 10$
$\frac{1}{2} B = 11° 19'$
$B = 22° 38'$

$\log r = 10.3010 - 10$
$\log (s - c) = \underline{0.3010}$
$\log \tan \frac{1}{2} C = 0.0000$
$\frac{1}{2} C = 45°$
$C = 90°$

First Check:
$A + B + C = 180° 1'$
Error $1'$

Second Check:

$$(a - b) \cos \tfrac{1}{2} C = c \sin \tfrac{1}{2} (A - B).$$
$$\log [(a - b) \cos \tfrac{1}{2} C] = 10.6946 - 10.$$
$$\log [c \sin \tfrac{1}{2} (A - B)] = 10.6944 - 10.$$

The following tabulation scheme is recommended for recording the results of Case IV.

Data and Results			Logarithms	
Given:	a	12	$\log (s - a)$	0.4771
	b	5	$\log (s - b)$	1.0000
	c	13	$\log (s - c)$	0.3010
			$\log s$	1.1761
Required:	$2s$	30	$\log r^2$	0.6020
	s	15	$\log r$	0.3010
	$s - a$	3	$\log K$	1.4771
	$s - b$	10	$\log a$	1.0792
	$s - c$	2	$\log b$	0.6990
	r	2	$\log c$	1.1139
	R	6.5	$\log R$	0.8129
	K	30	$\log \tan \tfrac{1}{2} A$	$9.8239 - 10$
	$\tfrac{1}{2} A$	33° 41.5'	$\log \tan \tfrac{1}{2} B$	$9.3010 - 10$
	$\tfrac{1}{2} B$	11° 19'	$\log \tan \tfrac{1}{2} C$	0.0000
	$\tfrac{1}{2} C$	45°		
	A	67° 23'		
	B	22° 38'		
	C	90°		

EXERCISE

Formulas:

$$r = \sqrt{\frac{(s - a)(s - b)(s - c)}{s}}.$$

$$\tan \tfrac{1}{2} A = \frac{r}{s - a}.$$

$$\tan \tfrac{1}{2} B = \frac{r}{s - b}.$$

$$\tan \tfrac{1}{2} C = \frac{r}{s - c}.$$

$$K = rs.$$

$$R = \frac{abc}{4K}.$$

SOLVING TRIANGLES BY THE USE OF LOGARITHMS

Data and Results			Logarithms
Given:	a	18	$\log(s-a)$
	b	15	$\log(s-b)$
	c	20	$\log(s-c)$
			$\log s$
Required:	$2s$		$\log r^2$
	s		$\log r$
	$s-a$		$\log K$
	$s-b$		$\log a$
	$s-c$		$\log b$
	r		$\log c$
	R		$\log R$
	K		$\log \tan \tfrac{1}{2} A$
	$\tfrac{1}{2} A$		$\log \tan \tfrac{1}{2} B$
	$\tfrac{1}{2} B$		$\log \tan \tfrac{1}{2} C$
	$\tfrac{1}{2} C$		
	A		
	B		
	C		

Remember that the half-angles are to be found to the nearest tenth of a minute.

First Check:
$$A + B + C = 180°.$$
Second Check:
$$(a - b) \cos \tfrac{1}{2} C = c \sin \tfrac{1}{2} (A - B).$$

EXERCISES

1. $A = 40° 20'$, $B = 72° 15'$, and $a = 14.8$. Find C, b, c, K, r, and R.

2. $B = 60° 26'$, $C = 20° 15'$, and $a = 10$. Find the remaining six parts.

3. $A = 67° 21'$, $B = 57° 48'$, and $b = 367$. Find the remaining six parts.

4. $a = 28.3$, $c = 20.5$, and $C = 62° 18'$. Find the remaining parts.

5. $b = 17.7$, $c = 21.6$, and $B = 34° 27'$. Find the remaining parts.

6. $b = 32$, $c = 48$, and $A = 46° 20'$. Find the side a. Use the cosine theorem.

7. $a = 18$, $b = 32$, and $C = 132° 24'$. Find the side c. Use the cosine theorem.

8. $a = 7.8$, $c = 8.34$, and $B = 68° 40'$. Find the remaining parts. Use the tangent theorem.

9. $b = 87.25$, $c = 63.27$, and $A = 75°$. Find the remaining parts.

10. $a = 12$, $b = 16$, and $c = 20$. Find the angles only. Use the cosine theorem.

11. $a = 10$, $b = 18$, and $c = 25$. Find the angles only.

12. $a = 34.1$, $b = 26$, and $c = 15.8$. Find the other six parts.

13. $a = 112$, $b = 150$, and $c = 50$. Find the other six parts.

14. $a = 1.728$, $b = 2.456$, and $c = 3.016$. Find the other six parts.

15. $a = 40$, $b = 48$, and $c = 52$. Find the other parts.

EXERCISES

1. An airplane is observed to be 10 miles from a station and to have a bearing of S. 50° E. It travels 22 miles in a direction N. 60° W. What is its distance and bearing from the station?

2. An airplane is flying due west at 75 miles per hour. At noon the pilot observes a signal tower to have a bearing of N. 20° E. At 12:20 P.M. the tower had a bearing of N. 50° E. Determine when the airplane was nearest the tower and its distance from the tower.

3. A steamer was headed due west, having a uniform speed. At 9 P.M. a lighthouse was observed to be S. 40° W. At 11 P.M. the bearing of the lighthouse was S. 40° E. The nearest distance of the steamer from the lighthouse was 8 miles. Find the speed of the steamer.

4. From one signal tower (A) two other signal towers (B and C) have bearings of S. 20° W. and S. 40° W. respectively. The distance from A to B is known to be 800 yards. The distance from B to C is 1000 yards. Required the distance from A to C.

5. A man starts at one station and rows a boat due east at a speed of 6 miles per hour. At the same time from another station bearing S. 30° W. and at a distance of one mile from the first station another man starts at a speed of 9 miles per hour. Assuming that neither boat changes its direction, in what direction should the second man start out to catch the first boat? How much time elapses before they meet?

6. A tree 60 feet high is on a hillside. The tree makes a shadow 80 feet long. At the end of the shadow the tree subtends an angle of 30°. Find the elevation of the sun.

SOLVING TRIANGLES BY THE USE OF LOGARITHMS

7. A swamp is between two observation stations (A and B). In order to determine the distance between A and B, another station (C) is chosen. From C the bearing of A is N. 70° E. and distant 422 yards. From C the bearing of B is S. 45° E. and its distance is 500 yards. Find the distance from A to B. (Use cosine theorem.)

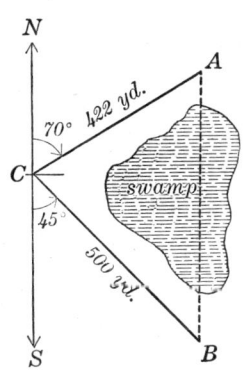

8. One railroad track bears N. 75° E. Another railroad track crosses the first and bears N. 10° E. At 12:35 P.M. a train on the first track passes the crossing at a speed of 45 miles per hour. Two minutes later a train on the second track passes the crossing at a speed of 60 miles per hour. How far apart will the trains be 15 minutes after the first train passes the crossing? (There are two solutions.)

9. Two trees stand on opposite sides of a lake. From a station (A) on a golf course, the distances of the trees are 800 yards and 600 yards. The bearings of the trees from the station are S. 10° W. and S. 70° E. Find the length of the lake. (Use tangent theorem.)

10. An observation station (B) is due east of a tower at (A). The angle of elevation of the tower is 54°. At a point (C) 100 yards south of the station, the angle of elevation of the tower is 36°. Find the height of the tower and the distance of the tower to the station.

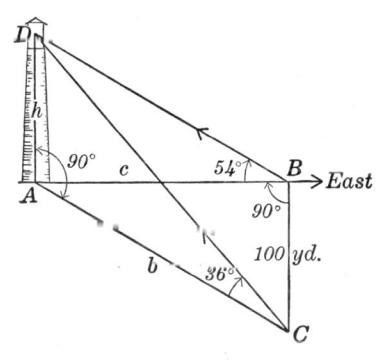

11. Using the formula for problem 36, page 44, show that
$$h = \frac{d \tan A \tan B}{\tan A - \tan B} = \frac{d \sin A \sin B}{\sin (A - B)}.$$

12. In exercise 11, find h when $d = 200$, $A = 50°$, and $B = 25°$.

13. A flagstaff is situated on the slope of a hill which is inclined at 10° to the horizontal. At a station (A) the angle of elevation of the top of the flagstaff is 35°. Walking 40 feet toward the base of the flagstaff to another station (B), we find that the angle of elevation of the top of the flagstaff is 65°. What is the height of the flagstaff and the distance of the station A to the base?

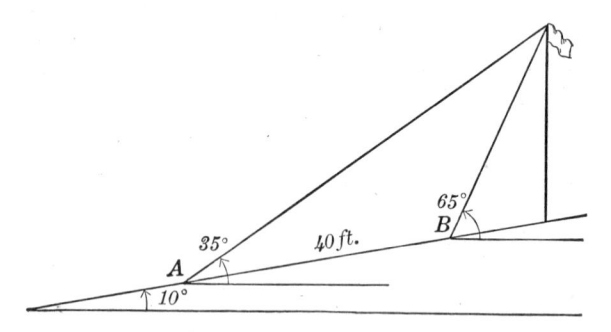

Horizontal distance between two inaccessible objects. Measure a base line AB. With a surveyor's transit it is possible to measure the angles ABC, ABD, BAC, and BAD. By using two applications of the sine theorem and one application of the tangent theorem, and then another application of the sine theorem, we are able to compute the horizontal distance between the inaccessible objects C and D.

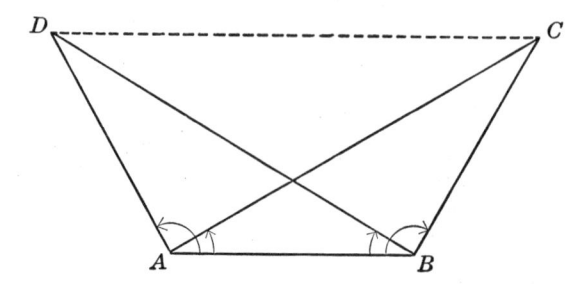

14. A surveying party is on one side of a river and desires to know the horizontal distance between two signal towers situated on the other side. A base line AB of 300 yards is measured. The angles measured are as follows: $ABC = 106°$, $ABD = 32°$, $BAC = 35°$, and $BAD = 100°$. Find the horizontal distance between the towers.

SOLVING TRIANGLES BY THE USE OF LOGARITHMS

75. Triangulation

In mountainous districts and along rocky coast lines it is often impossible to measure straight lines, but accessible points can be found from which angles to other accessible points can be measured. Also angles can be measured more accurately than lines. So there has been developed a system of land survey called *triangulation*. By this system it is necessary to measure only *one line* at the beginning of the survey as a base line, and one at the end as a check on the accuracy of the work. First an open level place is selected, and a base line is very accurately measured. From the ends of this line an accessible point is sighted and the angles measured. This triangle can be solved, and its sides will serve as new base lines from which points can be sighted, angles measured, new triangle solved, etc. As a check on the accuracy of the work, a side of the last triangle should always be *measured* and the measured length compared with the computed length.

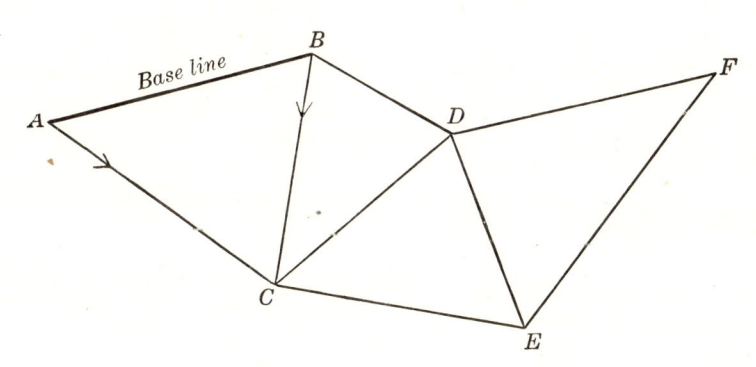

In the figure the base line AB is measured. Then the accessible point C is chosen, and the angles CAB and ABC are measured. By the Law of Sines the sides AC and BC can be computed. Next an accessible point D is selected which is visible from B and from C, and the angles DCB and CBD are measured. Then by use of the Law of Sines CD and BD can be calculated. Either one of these may now be used as a base line, etc. In the figure the transit has been set up at A, B, C, D, and E. EF or DF should be measured as a check on the accuracy of the work. The data secured is used in constructing a map of the region.

The method just described assumes that the surface of the earth is a plane. For very accurate surveying, adjustments are very carefully worked out which allow for the curvature of the earth. Below is a map prepared by triangulation.

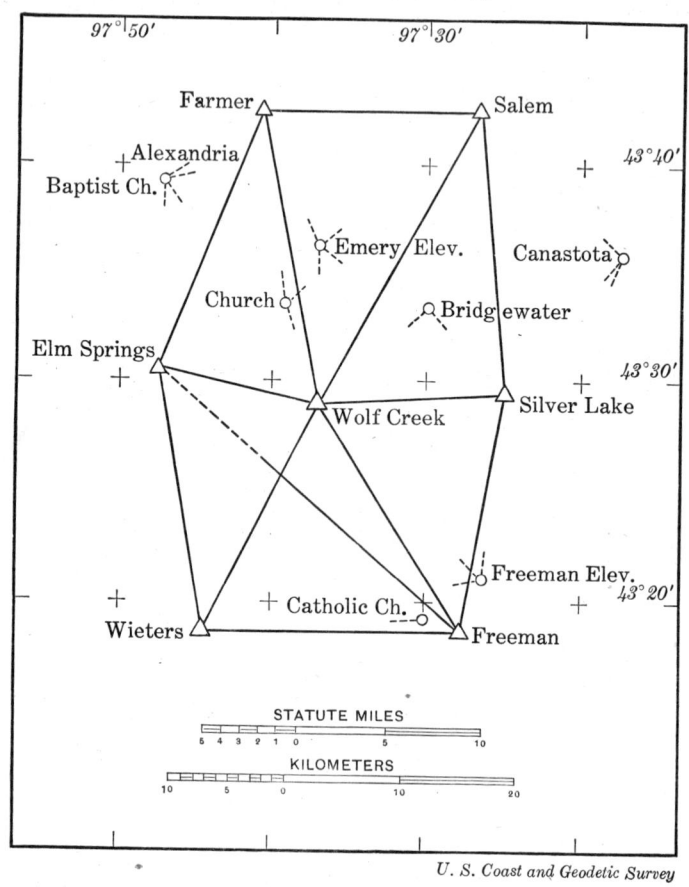

U. S. Coast and Geodetic Survey

REVIEW QUESTIONS ON CHAPTER VIII

1. Name the theorem to be used in solving the triangle in each of the following exercises. (Assume that logarithms are to be used.)
    (a) Given a, B, C.
    (b) Given a, b, A.
    (c) Given a, A, C.
    (d) Given a, c, A.
    (e) Given a, b, c.
    (f) Given C, b, c.

SOLVING TRIANGLES BY THE USE OF LOGARITHMS

2. When c, B, and C are known, write the formulas for finding a, b, A, K, r, R.

3. If b, c, and B are known, how may it be determined whether 0, 1, or 2 triangles are possible? List the formulas needed to solve the triangle (a) if there is only one solution, (b) if there are two solutions.

4. Given b, c, and A, what formulas are needed for finding a, B, C, r, R, K?

5. If a, b, and c are known, and it is required to use the tangent half-angle theorem, list the formulas needed to solve for r, A, B, C, K, R.

6. How many triangles are there which have the following parts:
    (a) $b = 25$, $c = 24$, $B = 60°$.
    (b) $a = 7$, $b = 10$, $A = 30°$.
    (c) $a = 14$, $b = 17$, $B = 30°$.
    (d) $a = 27$, $b = 22$, $B = 60°$.

7. In triangle ABC, $a = 32$, $b = 23$, $B = 32° 23'$. Solve the triangle. (2 solutions)

8. From an observation point A, an island subtends an angle of $42° 40'$. A is known to be 2375.2 feet from one end of the island and 4863.4 feet from the other end. Find the length of the island.

9. Draw triangle ABC, extend side BA to G and side AB to D. Plans were given to a road builder requiring the construction of a curved road tangent to AB at D and to AC at C. Observations had been made from point A determining angle CAG to be $46° 29'$. AC was known to be 475 feet. At the time construction was begun, floods had made point A inaccessible, and new observations had to be made from point B. Angle ABC was found to be $45° 26'$. Find the length of AB to determine how far the point of observation had to be moved.

10. In a certain machine, three wheels are tangent to each other at points A, B, and C. The centers are to be joined by a metal triangle. If the radii of the wheels are 2 inches, 3 inches, and 5 inches, find the angles at which the sides of the triangle meet. Use tangent half-angle theorem.

The Imaginary Number

THE history of mathematics reveals that man has been very slow in accepting new kinds of numbers. Fractions were long avoided through the use of denominate numbers; at first, surds were not understood, and negative numbers were considered as fictitious or impossible. So it is not surprising that Descartes (1637) should have given the name *imaginary* to the square root of a negative number.

In showing that there are two numbers, $5 + \sqrt{-15}$ and $5 - \sqrt{-15}$, whose sum is 10 and product 40, Cardan (1545) accomplished the multiplication of two complex numbers, but did nothing more with them. Girard (1629) said that the imaginary number must be recognized in order to generalize the rule for the number of roots of an equation.

A great impetus to the understanding of complex numbers was given by a graphic representation of them. Wallis (1673), an Englishman, made the beginning, and Wessel (1797), a Norwegian surveyor, was the first to give the modern presentation.

Euler (1748) first used the symbol i to designate $\sqrt{-1}$, and Gauss in 1832 gave the name *complex numbers* to numbers of the form $a + bi$. Early in the eighteenth century John Bernoulli and De Moivre introduced the imaginary number into trigonometry.

Today imaginary numbers are used freely in analysis, and in practical formulas for the transmission of electricity. It is interesting to note that Steinmetz, that genius in electricity, used j to represent $\sqrt{-1}$ to distinguish it from i, by which physicists designate the strength of an electric current.

The student will see that the so-called imaginary number has entirely outgrown the name given to it. Although other names have been suggested, the original persists.

CHAPTER

IX

Complex Numbers and De Moivre's Theorem

76. Complex numbers

THE study of complex numbers presents another application of trigonometry. Such numbers are used in formulas in the solution of equations, and in solving problems involving the application of *vector* geometry. The solutions of problems in many fields of advanced mathematics have been made easier by the use of complex numbers.

A new kind of number. In attempting to find the solution of the equation $x^2 + 2 = 0$ a new kind of number is met. Here $x^2 = -2$; so $x = \pm \sqrt{-2}$. The roots of the equation $x^2 - 3x + 3 = 0$ are $\dfrac{(3 \pm \sqrt{-3})}{2}$. The expressions $\sqrt{-2}$ and $\sqrt{-3}$ have a new unit. These numbers may be written $\sqrt{2}\sqrt{-1}$ and $\sqrt{3}\sqrt{-1}$. This new unit is $\sqrt{-1}$. This new unit is represented by the letter i. The numbers $\sqrt{2}\sqrt{-1}$ and $\sqrt{3}\sqrt{-1}$ are written $\sqrt{2}i$ and $\sqrt{3}i$. Numbers that are the products of i and real numbers are called *pure imaginary numbers*.

A *complex number is the sum of a real number and a pure imaginary number*. Thus, $\sqrt{3} \pm 2i$, $-2 \pm \sqrt{5}i$ are complex numbers. In the solutions of equations, complex numbers always appear in pairs. In general, numbers of the form $x + iy$, where x and y are real numbers, are called complex numbers.

Geometrical representation of complex numbers. To any real number, as 2, -3, $\sqrt{5}$, there corresponds a point on a line. To any complex number, as $x + iy$, there corresponds a point in a plane.

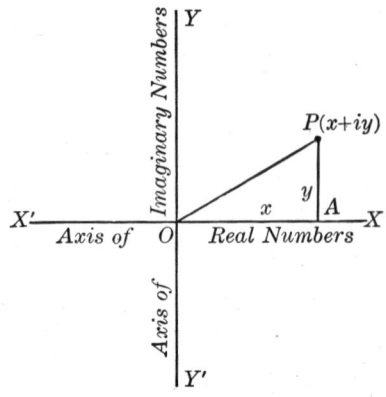

To locate a point P corresponding to the number $x + iy$, choose two perpendicular axes, $X'OX$ and $Y'OY$. $X'OX$ is called the *axis of real numbers*, and $Y'OY$ is called the *axis of imaginary numbers*. Since x is the real part of this complex number, $x + iy$, mark off x units on the axis of real numbers, thus obtaining the point A. On a line through A and perpendicular to OX mark off y units, thus obtaining the point P, which corresponds to the complex number $x + iy$. If z is the number represented by the point P, then

$$z = x + iy.$$

When $x = 0$, $z = iy$, which is a pure imaginary number. When $y = 0$, $z = x$, which is a real number. Hence a system of complex numbers includes all real numbers. Non-real complex numbers, that is, complex numbers in which y does not equal zero, are called *imaginary numbers*.

An interpretation of $\sqrt{-1}$ or i based on plane geometry. Using two

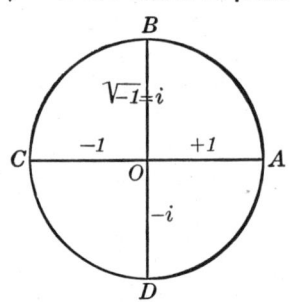

COMPLEX NUMBERS AND DE MOIVRE'S THEOREM

perpendicular lines, draw a circle having its center at their intersection and having a radius of unity, as shown in the figure. In plane geometry we have the theorem, *A perpendicular from any point in the circumference of a circle to a diameter is a mean proportional between the adjacent segments of the diameter*, and this would imply that $(OB)^2 = OA \times OC$. We assign to OA the value 1, and to OC the value -1. Substituting these values, the equation states that $(OB)^2 = (1)(-1) = -1$, which is true only when we assign to OB the value $\sqrt{-1}$ or i. Similarly we assign to OD, which extends in the opposite direction, the value $-i$.

Powers of i. When the unit line segment OA, to which we have assigned the value $+1$, has been revolved through one right angle in a counter-clockwise direction, it takes the position OB, which we have interpreted to represent $\sqrt{-1}$ or i.

$$\text{But } (+1) \times \sqrt{-1} = \sqrt{-1}.$$

Then we may associate revolving the line segment OA through one right angle in a counter-clockwise direction to the position OB, with multiplying $+1$ by $\sqrt{-1}$.

Now continue the revolution of OA through another right angle in the counter-clockwise direction. It now takes the position OC, which represents -1. We may associate this with the following:

$$(+1) \times \sqrt{-1} \times \sqrt{-1} = -1, \text{ or } i^2 = -1.$$

We will now postulate that with each successive revolution of the line segment OA through one right angle in a counter-clockwise direction, there may be associated one multiplication by $\sqrt{-1}$ or i. Then it is easy to see that

$$(+1) \times \sqrt{-1} \times \sqrt{-1} \times \sqrt{-1} = \sqrt{-1}, \text{ or } i^3 = -i$$

and $\quad (+1) \times \sqrt{-1} \times \sqrt{-1} \times \sqrt{-1} \times \sqrt{-1} = +1,$

or $i^4 = +1$.

Summarizing, we have

$$i^1 = i, \quad i^2 = -1, \quad i^3 = -i, \text{ and } i^4 = +1.$$

The student should continue the table through i^{12}.

Modulus of a complex number. In the figure on the next page the line OP is r units in length. This length is $\sqrt{x^2 + y^2}$ units and is called the *modulus* or *absolute value* of the number $x + iy$.

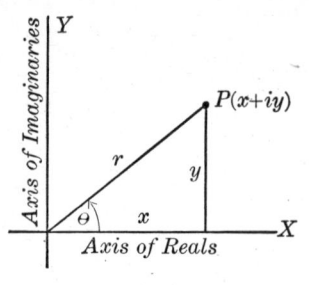

$$r = \sqrt{x^2 + y^2}.$$

The angle XOP, or θ, is called the *amplitude* or angle of the number $x + iy$. θ is the Greek letter "theta."

$$\theta = \tan^{-1}\left(\frac{y}{x}\right).$$

EXERCISES

1. Locate the following complex numbers: $2 + 2i$; $-2 + 3i$; $3 - 2i$; $3i$; $-4i$; $-1 - i$.

2. Find the modulus and amplitude of each number in exercise 1.

Addition of complex numbers. *Algebraic method.* Let the two complex numbers be $z = x + iy$ and $z' = x' + iy'$. Then
$$z + z' = (x + x') + i(y + y').$$
Combine the real parts of the numbers, and combine the imaginary parts of the numbers.

Example
$$(2 + 3i) + (-3 + 4i) = -1 + 7i.$$

Geometric method. Represent z by the point P and z' by the point P'. Construct the parallelogram $OPQP'$, having OP and OP' as adjacent sides. The point Q represents the number which is the sum of the numbers z and z'. In vector geometry we say that
$$\text{Vector } OQ = \text{Vector } OP + \text{Vector } OP'.$$

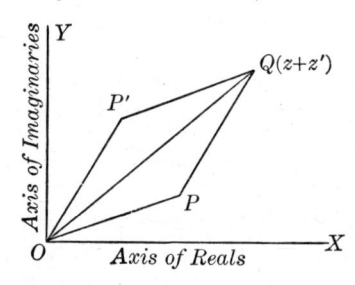

COMPLEX NUMBERS AND DE MOIVRE'S THEOREM

The difference of two complex numbers may be found in a similar manner. That is,
$$z - z' = (x - x') + i(y - y').$$
Make a geometrical construction to represent the difference of two complex numbers.

EXERCISES

Find the sum and difference of the following complex numbers, first algebraically, then geometrically

1. $z = 3 + 2i$ and $z' = 2 + 4i$.
2. $z = -3 + i$ and $z' = 2 - 2i$.
3. $z = 4 + 3i$ and $z' = -1 - 3i$.

Multiplication of complex numbers. *Algebraic method.*
$$z \times z' = (x + iy)(x' + iy').$$

Perform the indicated multiplication of the binomials and simplify the result.
Then
$$z \times z' = (xx' - yy') + i(xy' + x'y).$$

Example

Find the product of $(2 + 3i)$ and $(3 - 4i)$.
$$(2 + 3i)(3 - 4i) = [6 - (-12)] + i(-8 + 9) = 18 + i.$$

EXERCISE

Find the following products.

1. $(1 + 3i)(3 + 2i); (-2 + i)(2 - 3i); (-2 + 4i)(-3 - 2i)$.

77. Trigonometric form of complex numbers

In the figure, the complex number z is represented by the point P. We see that

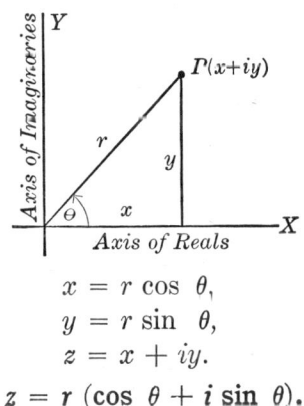

$$x = r \cos \theta,$$
$$y = r \sin \theta,$$
and
$$z = x + iy.$$
Hence,
$$z = r(\cos \theta + i \sin \theta).$$

Product of two complex numbers expressed in the trigonometric form.

$z \times z' = rr' (\cos \theta + i \sin \theta)(\cos \theta' + i \sin \theta')$.

$z \times z' = rr' [(\cos \theta \cos \theta' - \sin \theta \sin \theta') + i (\sin \theta \cos \theta' + \cos \theta \sin \theta')]$.

$z \times z' = rr' [\cos (\theta + \theta') + i \sin (\theta + \theta')]$.

Observe that:

The modulus of the product of two complex numbers equals the product of the moduli of the numbers. The amplitude of the product is equal to the sum of the amplitudes of the numbers.

Special products. When the factors of a product are equal, we get

$$z^2 = r^2 (\cos 2\theta + i \sin 2\theta),$$
$$z^3 = r^3 (\cos 3\theta + i \sin 3\theta).$$

When there are n equal factors,

$$z^n = r^n (\cos n\theta + i \sin n\theta).$$

78. De Moivre's theorem

When $r = 1$, $z = \cos \theta + i \sin \theta$. Substituting this value of z in the expression for the product of n equal factors, we get

$$(\cos \theta + i \sin \theta)^n = \cos n\theta + i \sin n\theta.$$

This relationship expresses the fact which is known as *De Moivre's theorem*. It can be shown that this theorem is true when n is a positive or negative integer or fraction.

EXAMPLES

1. Express $4 + 3i$ in trigonometric form.
$r = \sqrt{4^2 + 3^2} = 5$; $\tan \theta = \frac{3}{4}$.
$\sin \theta = \frac{3}{5}$ and $\cos \theta = \frac{4}{5}$.
$4 + 3i = 5 (\cos \theta + i \sin \theta)$.

2. Express $\sqrt{3} + i$ in trigonometric form.
$r = \sqrt{(\sqrt{3})^2 + 1^2} = 2$; $\tan \theta = \frac{1}{\sqrt{3}}$; $\theta = 30°$.
$\sqrt{3} + i = 2 (\cos 30° + i \sin 30°)$.

3. Express $13 (\cos \theta + i \sin \theta)$ in algebraic form, when $\tan \theta = \frac{5}{12}$.
$x = 13 \cos \theta = 13 (\frac{12}{13}) = 12$;
$y = 13 \sin \theta = 13 (\frac{5}{13}) = 5$.
$13 (\cos \theta + i \sin \theta) = 12 + 5i$.

EXERCISES

1. Express $1 + i$ in trigonometric form.
2. Express $1 + \sqrt{3}i$ in trigonometric form.

COMPLEX NUMBERS AND DE MOIVRE'S THEOREM

3. Express $-2 + 2i$ in trigonometric form.
4. Express $2(\cos 30° + i \sin 30°)$ in algebraic form.
5. Express $2(\cos 120° + i \sin 120°)$ in algebraic form.
6. Find the value of $(1 + i)^2$. *Hint:* $(1 + i)^2 = [\sqrt{2}(\cos 45° + i \sin 45°)]^2 = 2i$, by De Moivre's theorem.
7. Show trigonometrically that $(1 + i)^3 = -2 + 2i$.
8. Show trigonometrically that $(2 + 2i)^5 = -128 - 128i$.
9. Show trigonometrically that $(\cos 18° + i \sin 18°)^5 = i$.

Verify the following by the use of De Moivre's theorem.

10. $\left(\frac{1}{2} + \frac{\sqrt{3}}{2}i\right)^6 = 1$.
11. $(1 + \sqrt{3}i)^4 = -8 - 8\sqrt{3}i$.
12. $(1 + i)^6 = -8i$.
13. $(1 + i)^8 = 16$.
14. $(1 + i)^{12} = -64$.
15. $(-\sqrt{3} + i)^6 = -(2)^6$.
16. $\left(-\frac{1}{2} + \frac{\sqrt{3}}{2}i\right)^8 = -\frac{1}{2} - \frac{\sqrt{3}}{2}i$.
17. $(-i)^{10} = -1$.

79. Roots of complex numbers

To find the nth root of $z = x + iy$, we use De Moivre's theorem and write

$$z^{\frac{1}{n}} = r^{\frac{1}{n}}\left(\cos\frac{\theta}{n} + i\sin\frac{\theta}{n}\right).$$

The above relation will give only one root; so a more general form should be used.

$$z^{\frac{1}{n}} = r^{\frac{1}{n}}\left[\cos\frac{\theta + 2k\pi}{n} + i\sin\frac{\theta + 2k\pi}{n}\right],$$

where $k = 0, 1, 2, 3, \ldots, (n - 1)$. This gives n distinct roots.

EXAMPLES

1. Find the square root of 1.
$$z = x + iy = 1 = \cos 0° + i \sin 0°.$$
$$z^{\frac{1}{2}} = \cos\frac{0° + 2k\pi}{2} + i\sin\frac{0° + 2k\pi}{2}.$$

For $k = 0$, we get $z_1 = 1$; for $k = 1$, we get $z_2 = -1$.

2. Find the square root of $7 + 24i$.
$$z = 7 + 24i = 25(\cos\theta + i\sin\theta); \tan\theta = \tfrac{24}{7}.$$
$$z^{\frac{1}{2}} = 25^{\frac{1}{2}}\left[\cos\frac{\theta + 2k\pi}{2} + i\sin\frac{\theta + 2k\pi}{2}\right].$$

$$\cos\frac{\theta}{2} = \tfrac{4}{5} \text{ and } \sin\frac{\theta}{2} = \tfrac{3}{5}.$$

For $k = 0$, $z_1 = 5\left[\tfrac{4}{5} + i\tfrac{3}{5}\right] = 4 + 3i$.
For $k = 1$, $z_2 = 5\left[-\tfrac{4}{5} + i\left(-\tfrac{3}{5}\right)\right] = -4 - 3i$.

3. Find the square root of i.

$$z = x + iy = i = \cos 90° + i \sin 90°.$$

$$z^{\frac{1}{2}} = \cos\frac{90° + 2k\pi}{2} + i \sin\frac{90° + 2k\pi}{2}.$$

For $k = 0$, we get $z_1 = \cos 45° + i \sin 45° = \frac{\sqrt{2}}{2} + \frac{\sqrt{2}}{2}i$.

For $k = 1$, we get $z_2 = \cos 225° + i \sin 225° = -\frac{\sqrt{2}}{2} - \frac{\sqrt{2}}{2}i$.

EXERCISES

Find the square root of the following.
1. $4 + 3i$.
2. $3 + 4i$.
3. $5 + 12i$.
4. $3 - 4i$.

Solve the equations.
5. $x^3 - 1 = 0$. This means to find the three cube roots of $(+1)$.
6. $x^3 + 1 = 0$. This means to find the three cube roots of (-1).
7. Find the three cube roots of $-2 + 2i$.
8. Find the five fifth roots of 2^5.

Hint: $z = 2^5 = 2^5 (\cos 0° + i \sin 0°)$.

9. Find the six sixth roots of 2^6.
10. Find the five fifth roots of $(16 + 16\sqrt{3}i)$.

Hint: $z = 16 + 16\sqrt{3}i = 2^5 \left(\tfrac{1}{2} + \frac{\sqrt{3}}{2}i\right) = 2^5 (\cos 60° + i \sin 60°)$.

11. Solve the equation $x^8 = 256$.

REVIEW QUESTIONS ON CHAPTER IX

1. What new unit is used in each of the following numbers: $\sqrt{-2}, \sqrt{-16}, \sqrt{-a}, \sqrt{-a^2}$? Rewrite each of these numbers as a multiple of i.

2. What is a complex number? What is the general form of a complex number?

3. Make a table to show values of the powers of i to i^{12}. Using a graph, explain why these values recur in cycles of four.

4. Show the geometric representation of each of the following numbers: $-5 - 3i$; $2 + i$; $3i$; $2i + 3$.

Find the modulus and the amplitude of each.

COMPLEX NUMBERS AND DE MOIVRE'S THEOREM

5. Find the sum and difference of the following numbers, first algebraically, then geometrically:
  (a) $z = 2 + 3i$ and $z' = 3 - 2i$.
  (b) $z = -5 - i$ and $z' = 2i$.

6. Find the products of the following numbers:
  (a) $(-1 - 2i)(1 + 3i)$.
  (b) $(4 - i)(2 - 5i)$.

7. Express each of the following numbers in trigonometric form: $5 + 6i;\ 2 - i;\ -3 + 2i;\ 3i$.

8. Express each of the following in algebraic form:
  (a) $3(\cos 60° + i \sin 60°)$.
  (b) $2(\cos 0° + i \sin 0°)$.

9. Verify each of the following:
  (a) $(1 - i)^4 = -4$.
  (b) $(2 + 2i)^3 = 16(-1 + i)$.
  (c) $(-2 + 2i)^6 = 512i$.

10. Write the statement of De Moivre's theorem.

Use De Moivre's theorem in each of the following:

11. Find the four fourth roots of 1.

12. Find the square root of $-1 + \sqrt{3}i$.

13. Find all the roots of the equation $x^4 - 16i = 0$.

Summary of Formulas and Theorems

I. From Elementary Algebra and Geometry

1. When $ax^2 + bx + c = 0$, $x = \dfrac{-b \pm \sqrt{b^2 - 4ac}}{2a}$.
2. For a circle, $C = 2\pi r$ or πd.
3. For a circle, $A = \pi r^2$.
4. For a triangle, $A = \tfrac{1}{2}bh$.
5. A straight angle contains 180°.
6. The sum of the angles of a triangle is equal to a straight angle, or 180°.
7. An exterior angle of a triangle is equal to the sum of the opposite interior angles.
8. Two right triangles are congruent when
   (a) the hypotenuse and acute angle of one are equal respectively to the hypotenuse and acute angle of the other.
   (b) the hypotenuse and a leg of one are equal respectively to the hypotenuse and a leg of the other.
9. If two sides of a triangle are equal, the angles opposite the equal sides are equal.
10. If two angles of a triangle are equal, the sides opposite the equal angles are equal.
11. In an isosceles triangle the perpendicular from the vertex to the base bisects the base and the angle at the vertex.
12. In a 30°—60° right triangle the hypotenuse is double the side opposite the 30° angle.
13. When parallel lines are cut by a transversal, the alternate interior angles are equal, and the corresponding angles are equal.
14. If two sides of a triangle are unequal, the angle opposite the greater side is the greater.
15. If the sides of one angle are perpendicular (right to right, and left to left), the angles are equal.

16. A central angle has the same measure as its intercepted arc.

17. An inscribed angle has the same measure as one-half its intercepted arc.

18. An angle inscribed in a semicircle is a right angle.

19. In the same circle or in equal circles, equal arcs are subtended by equal chords.

20. Equal central angles intercept equal arcs.

21. Angles inscribed in the same segment of a circle, or in equal segments of the same circle, are equal.

22. Tangents drawn to a circle from an external point are equal, and make equal angles with the line joining that point to the center.

23. A tangent to a circle is perpendicular to the radius drawn to the point of contact.

24. Two triangles are similar when
    (a) two angles of one triangle are equal respectively to two angles of the other;
    (b) an angle of one triangle equals an angle of the other, and the including sides are proportional;
    (c) the ratios of the three pairs of corresponding sides are equal.

25. When triangles are similar
    (a) the corresponding angles are equal;
    (b) the ratios of the pairs of corresponding sides are equal.

26. In a right triangle ABC with hypotenuse c, $a^2 + b^2 = c^2$.

27. In any triangle, the square of a side opposite an acute angle is equal to the sum of the squares of the other two sides, diminished by twice the product of one of those sides by the projection of the other side on it.

28. In any obtuse triangle, the square of the side opposite an obtuse angle is equal to the sum of the squares of the other two sides, increased by twice the product of one of those sides by the projection of the other side on it.

II. From Trigonometry

RADIAN MEASURE FORMULAS

29. 2π radians $= 360°$ (p. 45)

SUMMARY OF FORMULAS AND THEOREMS 161

30. 1 radian = 57.3° (approximately) (p. 45)

31. $s = R \times A_r$ (p. 46)

32. $A_r = \dfrac{s}{R}$ (p. 47)

33. $R = \dfrac{s}{A_r}$ (p. 47)

34. For a sector of a circle,
$K = \tfrac{1}{2} R^2 \times A_r$ (p. 49)

35. For a segment of a circle,
$K = \tfrac{1}{2} R^2 (A_r - \sin A)$ (p. 49)

IMPORTANT TRIANGLE THEOREMS

36. $\dfrac{\sin A}{\sin B} = \dfrac{a}{b}$ (Sine Theorem) (p. 60)

37. $a^2 = b^2 + c^2 - 2bc \cos A$ (Cosine Theorem) (p. 63)

38. $\dfrac{\tan \tfrac{1}{2}(A - B)}{\tan \tfrac{1}{2}(A + B)} = \dfrac{a - b}{a + b}$ (Tangent Theorem) (p. 65)

39. $\tan \tfrac{1}{2} A = \dfrac{r}{s - a}$ (Tangent Half-angle Theorem) (p. 72)

$s = \dfrac{a + b + c}{2}$

40. $K = \tfrac{1}{2} bc \sin A$ (p. 68)

41. $K = \dfrac{a^2 \sin B \sin C}{2 \sin A}$ (p. 68)

42. $K = \sqrt{s(s-a)(s-b)(s-c)}$ (p. 69)

43. $K = rs$ (p. 69)

RADII OF INSCRIBED AND CIRCUMSCRIBED CIRCLES

44. $r = \sqrt{\dfrac{(s-a)(s-b)(s-c)}{s}}$ (p. 70)

45. $R = \dfrac{a}{2 \sin A}$ (p. 70)

$= \dfrac{ac}{2h}$

$= \dfrac{abc}{4K}$

EIGHT FUNDAMENTAL IDENTITIES

46. $\sin A = \dfrac{1}{\csc A}$ (p. 77)

47. $\cos A = \dfrac{1}{\sec A}$ (p. 77)

48. $\tan A = \dfrac{1}{\cot A}$ (p. 77)

49. $\sin^2 A + \cos^2 A = 1$ (p. 78)

50. $1 + \tan^2 A = \sec^2 A$ (p. 78)

51. $1 + \cot^2 A = \csc^2 A$ (p. 78)

52. $\tan A = \dfrac{\sin A}{\cos A}$ (p. 78)

53. $\cot A = \dfrac{\cos A}{\sin A}$ (p. 78)

FUNCTIONS OF THE SUM AND DIFFERENCE OF TWO ANGLES

54. $\sin(A + B) = \sin A \cos B + \cos A \sin B$ (p. 83)

55. $\cos(A + B) = \cos A \cos B - \sin A \sin B$ (p. 84)

56. $\tan(A + B) = \dfrac{\tan A + \tan B}{1 - \tan A \tan B}$ (p. 85)

57. $\sin(A - B) = \sin A \cos B - \cos A \sin B$ (p. 86)

58. $\cos(A - B) = \cos A \cos B + \sin A \sin B$ (p. 88)

59. $\tan(A - B) = \dfrac{\tan A - \tan B}{1 + \tan A \tan B}$ (p. 88)

FUNCTIONS OF A DOUBLE ANGLE

60. $\sin 2A = 2 \sin A \cos A$ (p. 90)

61. $\cos 2A = \cos^2 A - \sin^2 A$ (p. 91)

$ = 1 - 2 \sin^2 A$

$ = 2 \cos^2 A - 1$

62. $\tan 2A = \dfrac{2 \tan A}{1 - \tan^2 A}$ (p. 91)

FUNCTIONS OF HALF ANGLES

63. $\sin \tfrac{1}{2} A = \sqrt{\dfrac{1 - \cos A}{2}}$ (p. 92)

64. $\cos \tfrac{1}{2} A = \sqrt{\dfrac{1 + \cos A}{2}}$ (p. 92)

65. $\tan \tfrac{1}{2} A = \sqrt{\dfrac{1 - \cos A}{1 + \cos A}}$ (p. 93)

SUMMARY OF FORMULAS AND THEOREMS 163

THE SUM AND DIFFERENCE OF THE FUNCTIONS OF TWO ANGLES

66. $\sin A + \sin B = 2 \sin \dfrac{A+B}{2} \cos \dfrac{A-B}{2}$ (p. 94)

67. $\cos A + \cos B = 2 \cos \dfrac{A+B}{2} \cos \dfrac{A-B}{2}$ (p. 94)

68. $\sin A - \sin B = 2 \cos \dfrac{A+B}{2} \sin \dfrac{A-B}{2}$ (p. 94)

69. $\cos A - \cos B = -2 \sin \dfrac{A+B}{2} \sin \dfrac{A-B}{2}$ (p. 94)

LOGARITHM FORMULAS

70. $\log AB = \log A + \log B$ (p. 117)

71. $\log \dfrac{A}{B} = \log A - \log B$ (p. 117)

72. $\log N^x = x \log N$ (p. 117)

73. $\log \sqrt[n]{N} = \dfrac{1}{n} \log N$ (p. 117)

COMPLEX NUMBER FORMULAS

74. $(\cos \theta + i \sin \theta)^n = \cos n\theta + i \sin n\theta$ (p. 154)
    (De Moivre's Theorem)

75. $(\cos \theta + i \sin \theta)^{\frac{1}{n}} = \cos \dfrac{\theta + 2k\pi}{n} + i \sin \dfrac{\theta + 2k\pi}{n}$ (p. 155)

$k = 0, 1, \ldots n - 1$.

FUNCTIONS OF SOME IMPORTANT ANGLES

76. $\sin 0° = 0$ $\cos 0° = 1$ $\tan 0° = 0$

77. $\sin 30° = \tfrac{1}{2}$ $\cos 30° = \tfrac{1}{2}\sqrt{3}$ $\tan 30° = \dfrac{1}{\sqrt{3}}$ or $\tfrac{1}{3}\sqrt{3}$

78. $\sin 45° = \tfrac{1}{2}\sqrt{2}$ $\cos 45° = \tfrac{1}{2}\sqrt{2}$ $\tan 45° = 1$

79. $\sin 60° = \tfrac{1}{2}\sqrt{3}$ $\cos 60° = \tfrac{1}{2}$ $\tan 60° = \sqrt{3}$

80. $\sin 90° = 1$ $\cos 90° = 0$ $\tan 90° = \infty$

Table I. Natural Trigonometric Functions

Angle	Sin A	Cos A	Tan A	Cot A	
0°	0.0000	1.0000	0.0000	∞	**90°**
1°	.0175	.9998	.0175	57.2900	89°
2°	.0349	.9994	.0349	28.6363	88°
3°	.0523	.9986	.0524	19.0811	87°
4°	.0698	.9976	.0699	14.3007	86°
5°	.0872	.9962	.0875	11.4301	**85°**
6°	.1045	.9945	.1051	9.5144	84°
7°	.1219	.9925	.1228	8.1443	83°
8°	.1392	.9903	.1405	7.1154	82°
9°	.1564	.9877	.1584	6.3138	81°
10°	.1736	.9848	.1763	5.6713	**80°**
11°	.1908	.9816	.1944	5.1446	79°
12°	.2079	.9781	.2126	4.7046	78°
13°	.2250	.9744	.2309	4.3315	77°
14°	.2419	.9703	.2493	4.0108	76°
15°	.2588	.9659	.2679	3.7321	**75°**
16°	.2756	.9613	.2867	3.4874	74°
17°	.2924	.9563	.3057	3.2709	73°
18°	.3090	.9511	.3249	3.0777	72°
19°	.3256	.9455	.3443	2.9042	71°
20°	.3420	.9397	.3640	2.7475	**70°**
21°	.3584	.9336	.3839	2.6051	69°
22°	.3746	.9272	.4040	2.4751	68°
23°	.3907	.9205	.4245	2.3559	67°
24°	.4067	.9135	.4452	2.2460	66°
25°	.4226	.9063	.4663	2.1445	**65°**
26°	.4384	.8988	.4877	2.0503	64°
27°	.4540	.8910	.5095	1.9626	63°
28°	.4695	.8829	.5317	1.8807	62°
29°	.4848	.8746	.5543	1.8040	61°
30°	.5000	.8660	.5774	1.7321	**60°**
31°	.5150	.8572	.6009	1.6643	59°
32°	.5299	.8480	.6249	1.6003	58°
33°	.5446	.8387	.6494	1.5399	57°
34°	.5592	.8290	.6745	1.4826	56°
35°	.5736	.8192	.7002	1.4281	**55°**
36°	.5878	.8090	.7265	1.3764	54°
37°	.6018	.7986	.7536	1.3270	53°
38°	.6157	.7880	.7813	1.2799	52°
39°	.6293	.7771	.8098	1.2349	51°
40°	.6428	.7660	.8391	1.1918	**50°**
41°	.6561	.7547	.8693	1.1504	49°
42°	.6691	.7431	.9004	1.1106	48°
43°	.6820	.7314	.9325	1.0724	47°
44°	.6947	.7193	.9657	1.0355	46°
45°	.7071	.7071	1.0000	1.0000	**45°**
	Cos A	Sin A	Cot A	Tan A	Angle

CONDENSED TABLES

Table II. Logarithms of Numbers

N	0	1	2	3	4	5	6	7	8	9
10	0000	0043	0086	0128	0170	0212	0253	0294	0334	0374
11	0414	0453	0492	0531	0569	0607	0645	0682	0719	0755
12	0792	0828	0864	0899	0934	0969	1004	1038	1072	1106
13	1139	1173	1206	1239	1271	1303	1335	1367	1399	1430
14	1461	1492	1523	1553	1584	1614	1644	1673	1703	1732
15	1761	1790	1818	1847	1875	1903	1931	1959	1987	2014
16	2041	2068	2095	2122	2148	2175	2201	2227	2253	2279
17	2304	2330	2355	2380	2405	2430	2455	2480	2504	2529
18	2553	2577	2601	2625	2648	2672	2695	2718	2742	2765
19	2788	2810	2833	2856	2878	2900	2923	2945	2967	2989
20	3010	3032	3054	3075	3096	3118	3139	3160	3181	3201
21	3222	3243	3263	3284	3304	3324	3345	3365	3385	3404
22	3424	3444	3464	3483	3502	3522	3541	3560	3579	3598
23	3617	3636	3655	3674	3692	3711	3729	3747	3766	3784
24	3802	3820	3838	3856	3874	3892	3909	3927	3945	3962
25	3979	3997	4014	4031	4048	4065	4082	4099	4116	4133
26	4150	4166	4183	4200	4216	4232	4249	4265	4281	4298
27	4314	4330	4346	4362	4378	4393	4409	4425	4440	4456
28	4472	4487	4502	4518	4533	4548	4564	4579	4594	4609
29	4624	4639	4654	4669	4683	4698	4713	4728	4742	4757
30	4771	4786	4800	4814	4829	4843	4857	4871	4886	4900
31	4914	4928	4942	4955	4969	4983	4997	5011	5024	5038
32	5051	5065	5079	5092	5105	5119	5132	5145	5159	5172
33	5185	5198	5211	5224	5237	5250	5263	5276	5289	5302
34	5315	5328	5340	5353	5366	5378	5391	5403	5416	5428
35	5441	5453	5465	5478	5490	5502	5514	5527	5539	5551
36	5563	5575	5587	5599	5611	5623	5635	5647	5658	5670
37	5682	5694	5705	5717	5729	5740	5752	5763	5775	5786
38	5798	5809	5821	5832	5843	5855	5866	5877	5888	5899
39	5911	5922	5933	5944	5955	5966	5977	5988	5999	6010
40	6021	6031	6042	6053	6064	6075	6085	6096	6107	6117
41	6128	6138	6149	6160	6170	6180	6191	6201	6212	6222
42	6232	6243	6253	6263	6274	6284	6294	6304	6314	6325
43	6335	6345	6355	6365	6375	6385	6395	6405	6415	6425
44	6435	6444	6454	6464	6474	6484	6493	6503	6513	6522
45	6532	6542	6551	6561	6571	6580	6590	6599	6609	6618
46	6628	6637	6646	6656	6665	6675	6684	6693	6702	6712
47	6721	6730	6739	6749	6758	6767	6776	6785	6794	6803
48	6812	6821	6830	6839	6848	6857	6866	6875	6884	6893
49	6902	6911	6920	6928	6937	6946	6955	6964	6972	6981
50	6990	6998	7007	7016	7024	7033	7042	7050	7059	7067
51	7076	7084	7093	7101	7110	7118	7126	7135	7143	7152
52	7160	7168	7177	7185	7193	7202	7210	7218	7226	7235
53	7243	7251	7259	7267	7275	7284	7292	7300	7308	7316
54	7324	7332	7340	7348	7356	7364	7372	7380	7388	7396

Table II. Logarithms of Numbers—Continued

N	0	1	2	3	4	5	6	7	8	9
55	7404	7412	7419	7427	7435	7443	7451	7459	7466	7474
56	7482	7490	7497	7505	7513	7520	7528	7536	7543	7551
57	7559	7566	7574	7582	7589	7597	7604	7612	7619	7627
58	7634	7642	7649	7657	7664	7672	7679	7686	7694	7701
59	7709	7716	7723	7731	7738	7745	7752	7760	7767	7774
60	7782	7789	7796	7803	7810	7818	7825	7832	7839	7846
61	7853	7860	7868	7875	7882	7889	7896	7903	7910	7917
62	7924	7931	7938	7945	7952	7959	7966	7973	7980	7987
63	7993	8000	8007	8014	8021	8028	8035	8041	8048	8055
64	8062	8069	8075	8082	8089	8096	8102	8109	8116	8122
65	8129	8136	8142	8149	8156	8162	8169	8176	8182	8189
66	8195	8202	8209	8215	8222	8228	8235	8241	8248	8254
67	8261	8267	8274	8280	8287	8293	8299	8306	8312	8319
68	8325	8331	8338	8344	8351	8357	8363	8370	8376	8382
69	8388	8395	8401	8407	8414	8420	8426	8432	8439	8445
70	8451	8457	8463	8470	8476	8482	8488	8494	8500	8506
71	8513	8519	8525	8531	8537	8543	8549	8555	8561	8567
72	8573	8579	8585	8591	8597	8603	8609	8615	8621	8627
73	8633	8639	8645	8651	8657	8663	8669	8675	8681	8686
74	8692	8698	8704	8710	8716	8722	8727	8733	8739	8745
75	8751	8756	8762	8768	8774	8779	8785	8791	8797	8802
76	8808	8814	8820	8825	8831	8837	8842	8848	8854	8859
77	8865	8871	8876	8882	8887	8893	8899	8904	8910	8915
78	8921	8927	8932	8938	8943	8949	8954	8960	8965	8971
79	8976	8982	8987	8993	8998	9004	9009	9015	9020	9025
80	9031	9036	9042	9047	9053	9058	9063	9069	9074	9079
81	9085	9090	9096	9101	9106	9112	9117	9122	9128	9133
82	9138	9143	9149	9154	9159	9165	9170	9175	9180	9186
83	9191	9196	9201	9206	9212	9217	9222	9227	9232	9238
84	9243	9248	9253	9258	9263	9269	9274	9279	9284	9289
85	9294	9299	9304	9309	9315	9320	9325	9330	9335	9340
86	9345	9350	9355	9360	9365	9370	9375	9380	9385	9390
87	9395	9400	9405	9410	9415	9420	9425	9430	9435	9440
88	9445	9450	9455	9460	9465	9469	9474	9479	9484	9489
89	9494	9499	9504	9509	9513	9518	9523	9528	9533	9538
90	9542	9547	9552	9557	9562	9566	9571	9576	9581	9586
91	9590	9595	9600	9605	9609	9614	9619	9624	9628	9633
92	9638	9643	9647	9652	9657	9661	9666	9671	9675	9680
93	9685	9689	9694	9699	9703	9708	9713	9717	9722	9727
94	9731	9736	9741	9745	9750	9754	9759	9763	9768	9773
95	9777	9782	9786	9791	9795	9800	9805	9809	9814	9818
96	9823	9827	9832	9836	9841	9845	9850	9854	9859	9863
97	9868	9872	9877	9881	9886	9890	9894	9899	9903	9908
98	9912	9917	9921	9926	9930	9934	9939	9943	9948	9952
99	9956	9961	9965	9969	9974	9978	9983	9987	9991	9996

CONDENSED TABLES

Table III. Logarithms of Trigonometric Functions

Angle	log sin	log tan	log cot	log cos	
0°	......	......	......	0.0000	90°
1°	8.2419	8.2419	1.7581	9.9999	89°
2°	8.5428	8.5431	1.4569	9.9997	88°
3°	8.7188	8.7194	1.2806	9.9994	87°
4°	8.8436	8.8446	1.1554	9.9989	86°
5°	8.9403	8.9420	1.0580	9.9983	85°
6°	9.0192	9.0216	0.9784	9.9976	84°
7°	9.0859	9.0891	0.9109	9.9968	83°
8°	9.1436	9.1478	0.8522	9.9958	82°
9°	9.1943	9.1997	0.8003	9.9946	81°
10°	9.2397	9.2463	0.7537	9.9934	80°
11°	9.2806	9.2887	0.7113	9.9919	79°
12°	9.3179	9.3275	0.6725	9.9904	78°
13°	9.3521	9.3634	0.6366	9.9887	77°
14°	9.3837	9.3968	0.6032	9.9869	76°
15°	9.4130	9.4281	0.5719	9.9849	75°
16°	9.4403	9.4575	0.5425	9.9828	74°
17°	9.4659	9.4853	0.5147	9.9806	73°
18°	9.4900	9.5118	0.4882	9.9782	72°
19°	9.5126	9.5370	0.4630	9.9757	71°
20°	9.5341	9.5611	0.4389	9.9730	70°
21°	9.5543	9.5842	0.4158	9.9702	69°
22°	9.5736	9.6064	0.3936	9.9672	68°
23°	9.5919	9.6279	0.3721	9.9640	67°
24°	9.6093	9.6486	0.3514	9.9607	66°
25°	9.6259	9.6687	0.3313	9.9573	65°
26°	9.6418	9.6882	0.3118	9.9537	64°
27°	9.6570	9.7072	0.2928	9.9499	63°
28°	9.6716	9.7257	0.2743	9.9459	62°
29°	9.6856	9.7438	0.2562	9.9418	61°
30°	9.6990	9.7614	0.2386	9.9375	60°
31°	9.7118	9.7788	0.2212	9.9331	59°
32°	9.7242	9.7958	0.2042	9.9284	58°
33°	9.7361	9.8125	0.1875	9.9236	57°
34°	9.7476	9.8290	0.1710	9.9186	56°
35°	9.7586	9.8452	0.1548	9.9134	55°
36°	9.7692	9.8613	0.1387	9.9080	54°
37°	9.7795	9.8771	0.1229	9.9023	53°
38°	9.7893	9.8928	0.1072	9.8965	52°
39°	9.7989	9.9084	0.0916	9.8905	51°
40°	9.8081	9.9238	0.0762	9.8843	50°
41°	9.8169	9.9392	0.0608	9.8778	49°
42°	9.8255	9.9544	0.0456	9.8711	48°
43°	9.8338	9.9697	0.0303	9.8641	47°
44°	9.8418	9.9848	0.0152	9.8569	46°
45°	9.8495	0.0000	0.0000	9.8495	45°
	log cos	log cot	log tan	log sin	Angle

Explanation of Expanded Tables

Table IV gives the values of the sines, tangents, cotangents, and cosines of each angle from 0° to 90° at intervals of 10′. To find the functions of angles less than 45°, find the angle size in the left-hand column and use the function name at the top of the function columns. To find the functions of angles greater than 45° and less than 90°, find the angle size in the right-hand column and use the function name at the bottom of the function columns.

Table V gives the mantissas of the logarithms of integers from 1 to 999 inclusive. The characteristic of a logarithm is to be obtained by the rule for characteristics (text, p. 116).

How to use logarithms is explained in the text, Chapter VII, Sections 63 to 66 inclusive.

Table VI gives the logarithms of the sines, tangents, cotangents, and cosines of angles from 0° to 90° at intervals of 10′. The table is to be read and used in the same manner as Table IV.

1. How to find the sine and tangent of an angle directly from the table

EXAMPLES

1. Find the value of sin 18° 20′.

Find 18° 20′ in the left-hand column. To the right in the column headed "Sin A" find .3145. Then sin 18° 20′ = .3145.

2. Find the value of tan 42° 40′.

Find 42° 40′ in the left-hand column. To the right in the column headed "Tan A" find .9217. Then tan 42° 40′ = .9217.

3. Find the value of sin 74° 30′.

Find 74° 30′ in the right-hand column. To the left in the column with "Sin A" at the bottom find .9636. Then sin 74° 30′ = .9636.

4. Find the value of tan 56° 10′.

Find 56° 10′ in the right-hand column. To the left in the column with "Tan A" at the bottom find 1.4919. Then tan 56° 10′ = 1.4919.

EXPLANATION OF EXPANDED TABLES 169

2. How to find the sine and tangent of an angle involving any number of minutes

EXAMPLES

1. Find   sin 18° 23'.
The given angle is between 18° 20' and 18° 30'.

$$\begin{aligned} \sin 18° 30' &= .3173. \\ \sin 18° 20' &= .3145. \\ \text{difference} & .0028. \end{aligned}$$

Assume that the change in the angle makes an approximately corresponding change in the function. Then the correction for 3' is ($\frac{3}{10}$) of .0028), which equals .0008. Since the sine function increases as the angle increases to 90°, *add* the correction to the sine of 18° 20'.

$$.3145 + .0008 = .3153.$$
$$\sin 18° 23' = .3153.$$

Note: The correction for 3' may be considered as $\frac{3}{10}$ of 28, or 8. Then add 8 to 3145, which gives the same sequence of figures as in the above.

2. Find   tan 49° 47'.
The given angle is between 49° 40' and 49° 50'.

$$\begin{aligned} \tan 49° 50' &= 1.1847. \\ \tan 49° 40' &= 1.1778. \\ \text{difference} & .0069. \end{aligned}$$

Add $\frac{7}{10}$ of .0069 to the tangent of 49° 40'.

$$1.1778 + .0048 = 1.1826.$$
$$\tan 49° 47' = 1.1826.$$

Note: Observe that the *correction is added* when finding the *sine* or the *tangent* of an angle involving minutes.

EXERCISES

Verify the following values.
1. sin 34° 24' = .5650.
2. sin 54° 42' = .8161.
3. tan 16° 36' = .2981.
4. tan 62° 17' = 1.9034.

$\frac{4}{10} \times 24 = 9.6$ or 10.
$\frac{2}{10} \times 17 = 3.4$ or 3.
$\frac{6}{10} \times 32 = 19.2$ or 19.
$\frac{7}{10} \times 134 = 93.8$ or 94.

3. How to find the cosine and cotangent of an angle involving minutes

EXAMPLES

1. Find cos 25° 38′.

The given angle is between 25° 30′ and 25° 40′.

$$\cos 25° 40' = .9013.$$
$$\cos 25° 30' = .9026.$$
$$\text{difference } \overline{.0013.}$$

The correction for 8′ is ($\frac{8}{10}$ of .0013), or .0010. Since the cosine function decreases as the angle increases, *subtract* the correction from the cosine of 25° 30′.

$$\cos 25° 38' = .9026 - .0010 = .9016.$$

2. Find cot 55° 24′.

The given angle is between 55° 20′ and 55° 30′.

$$\cot 55° 30' = .6873.$$
$$\cot 55° 20' = .6916.$$
$$\text{difference } \overline{.0043}$$

$$\cot 55° 24' = .6916 - (\tfrac{4}{10} \text{ of } .0043) = .6899.$$

Note: Observe that the *correction is subtracted* when finding the *cosine* or the *cotangent* of an angle involving minutes.

EXERCISES

Verify the following values.

1. cos 72° 45′ = .2965.
2. cos 28° 17′ = .8806.
3. cot 34° 56′ = 1.4317.
4. cot 68° 13′ = .3996.

$\tfrac{5}{10} \times 27 = 13.5$ or 14.
$\tfrac{7}{10} \times 14 = 9.8$ or 10.
$\tfrac{6}{10} \times 89 = 53.4$ or 53.
$\tfrac{3}{10} \times 33 = 9.9$ or 10.

4. Given a function of an angle, to find the angle

EXAMPLES

1. Sin A = .6352; find angle A.

Reading down the sine column, we observe that .6352 is between .6338 and .6361.

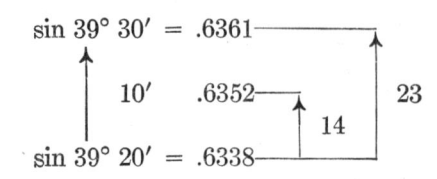

$$\sin 39° 30' = .6361$$
10′   .6352   23
                14
$$\sin 39° 20' = .6338$$

EXPLANATION OF EXPANDED TABLES

A difference of 23 in the table makes a difference of $10'$ in the angle. Then a difference of 14 in the table will make a difference of $\frac{14}{23}$ of $10'$ in the angle. $\frac{14}{23}$ of $10' = 6'$. Then $A = 39°\ 20' + 6' = 39°\ 26'$.

2. Tan $A = 1.4262$; find angle A.

Reading up the column having "Tan A" at the bottom, we observe that 1.4262 is between 1.4193 and 1.4281.

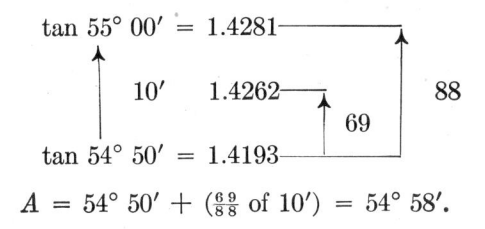

$$\tan 55°\ 00' = 1.4281$$
$$\tan 54°\ 50' = 1.4193$$

$A = 54°\ 50' + (\frac{69}{88} \text{ of } 10') = 54°\ 58'$.

EXERCISES

Verify the following angles.

1. $\sin A = .4728$. $A = 28°\ 13'$. $\frac{8}{26} \times 10' = 3'$.
2. $\sin A = .7630$. $A = 49°\ 44'$. $\frac{7}{19} \times 10' = 4'$.
3. $\tan A = .3524$. $A = 19°\ 25'$. $\frac{16}{33} \times 10' = 5'$.
4. $\tan A = 2.4184$. $A = 67°\ 32'$. $\frac{42}{200} \times 10' = 2'$.

Examples

3. Cos $A = .7246$; find angle A.

Reading down the cosine column, observe that .7246 is between .7254 and .7234.

$$\cos 43°\ 40' = .7234$$
$$\cos 43°\ 30' = .7254$$

$A = 43°\ 30' + (\frac{8}{20} \times 10') = 43°\ 34'$.

4. Cot $A = .4801$; find angle A.

Reading up the column which has "Cot A" at the bottom, observe that .4801 is between .4806 and .4770.

$$\cot 64°\ 30' = .4770$$
$$\cot 64°\ 20' = .4806$$

$A = 64°\ 20' + (\frac{5}{36} \times 10') = 64°\ 21'$.

EXERCISES

Verify the following angles.
1. $\cos A = .4428$. $\quad A = 63° 43'$. $\quad \frac{8}{26} \times 10' = 3'$.
2. $\cos A = .7891$. $\quad A = 37° 54'$. $\quad \frac{7}{18} \times 10' = 4'$.
3. $\cot A = 1.2562$. $\quad A = 38° 31'$. $\quad \frac{10}{75} \times 10' = 1'$.
4. $\cot A = .6032$. $\quad A = 58° 54'$. $\quad \frac{16}{39} \times 10' = 4'$.

5. How to find the logarithm of a number not specifically given in the table

EXAMPLE

Find the logarithm of 4863.

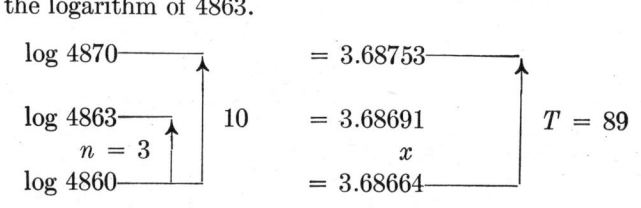

$$
\begin{array}{llll}
\log 4870 & & = 3.68753 & \\
\log 4863 & 10 & = 3.68691 & T = 89 \\
n = 3 & & x & \\
\log 4860 & & = 3.68664 &
\end{array}
$$

It is not necessary to read the mantissa as a decimal.

We see that a difference of 10 in the number makes a difference of 89 (T) in the table. A difference of 3 (n) in the number will make what difference (x) in the table? We shall assume that the change in the numbers is proportional to the change in the table. This assumption is not correct, but sufficiently accurate for most computations. A difference of 3 in the number will make a difference of $\frac{3}{10}$ of 89 in the table. $\frac{3}{10}$ of $89 = 26.7$. Add 27 to the logarithm of 4860.

For a four-figure number the *additive correction* is

$$x = \frac{n}{10} \times T.$$

For a five-figure number the *additive correction* is

$$x = \frac{n}{100} \times T.$$

EXERCISES

Verify the following.
1. $\log 24.96 = 1.39724$. $\quad \frac{6}{10} \times 174 = 104.4$ or 104.
2. $\log 354.2 = 2.54925$. $\quad \frac{2}{10} \times 123 = 24.6$ or 25.
3. $\log .3486 = 9.54233 - 10$. $\quad \frac{6}{10} \times 125 = 75$.
4. $\log 3.493 = 0.54320$. $\quad \frac{3}{10} \times 124 = 37.2$ or 37.
5. $\log 846.25 = 2.92750$. $\quad \frac{25}{100} \times 51 = 12.75$ or 13.
6. $\log .018438 = 8.26571 - 10$. $\quad \frac{38}{100} \times 235 = 89.3$ or 89.

6. How to find a number corresponding to a given logarithm

EXAMPLE

Given $\log N = 2.46932$; find N.

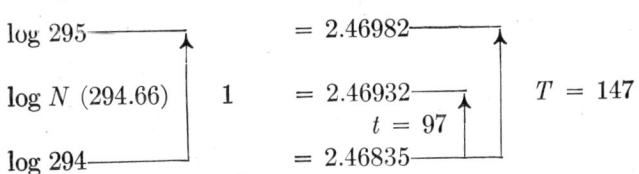

$$\log 295 = 2.46982$$
$$\log N\ (294.66) \quad 1 \quad = 2.46932 \qquad T = 147$$
$$\qquad\qquad\qquad\qquad\qquad t = 97$$
$$\log 294 = 2.46835$$

If a difference of 147 (T) in the table makes a difference of 1 in the number, then a difference of 97 (t) in the table will make a difference of $\frac{97}{147}$ of 1 in the number. $\frac{97}{147}$ of $1 = .66$.

Annex .66 to 294. A characteristic of 2 means that there are three figures to the left of the decimal point in the number.

Instead of dealing with decimal parts for the differences of the number, it is convenient to think in terms of a three-figure number. In the above example the 66 was annexed to the right of 294, and then the number was pointed off for the characteristic 2.

The *annexed part* of the number is expressed by

$$n = \frac{t}{T}.$$

EXERCISES

Verify the following.

1. $\log N = 2.63824$. $N = 434.75$. $\frac{75}{100} = .75$.
2. $\log N = 9.86468 - 10$. $N = .73229$. $\frac{17}{59} = .29$.
3. $\log N = 3.18462$. $N = 1529.754$. $\frac{278}{285} = .9754$.
4. $\log N = 1.01787$. $N = 10.42$. $\frac{84}{416} = .20$.
5. $\log N = 0.46342$. $N = 2.91$. $\frac{102}{149} = .68$.
6. $\log N = 8.64078 - 10$. $N = .0437$. $\frac{30}{99} = .30$.

Note: When negative numbers appear in a computation, the sign of the result is determined by the algebraic laws of signs. Make the computation, using the logarithms of all the numbers considered as positive, and then determine the sign of the result.

7. How to find logarithms of trigonometric functions

EXAMPLES

1. Find $\log \sin 18°\ 24'$.
The given angle is between $18°\ 20'$ and $18°\ 30'$.

PLANE TRIGONOMETRY

log sin 18° 30' = 9.50148 − 10

log sin 18° 24'   10' = 9.49920 − 10 $T = 380$

$m = 4'$

log sin 18° 20' = 9.49768 − 10

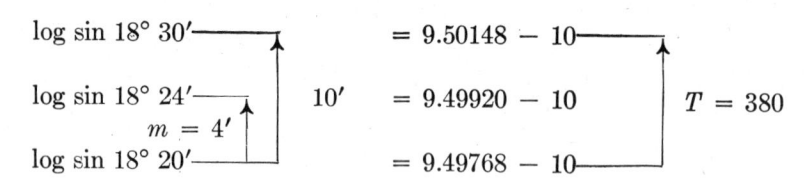

If 10' make a difference of 380 in the table, then 4' will make a difference of $\frac{4}{10}$ of 380 in the table. $\frac{4}{10}$ of 380 = 152. Add .00152 to the log sin 18° 20'.

If m is the number of minutes for which interpolation is made, then the correction to be *added* is

$$\frac{m}{10} \times T.$$

The same method is used in finding the "log tan."

EXERCISES

Verify the following logarithms.

1. log sin 25° 32' = 9.63451 − 10. $\frac{2}{10} \times 264 = 52.8$ or 53.
2. log sin 35° 43' = 9.76625 − 10. $\frac{3}{10} \times 175 = 52.5$ or 53.
3. log sin 48° 28' = 9.87424 − 10. $\frac{8}{10} \times 112 = 89.6$ or 90.
4. log sin 62° 45' = 9.94891 − 10. $\frac{5}{10} \times 65 = 32.5$ or 33.
5. log sin 4° 53' = 8.93002 − 10. $\frac{3}{10} \times 1469 = 440.7$ or 441.
6. log tan 18° 12' = 9.51691 − 10. $\frac{2}{10} \times 425 = 85.$
7. log tan 48° 18' = 10.05014 − 10. $\frac{8}{10} \times 255 = 204.$
8. log tan 4° 45' = 8.91951 − 10. $\frac{5}{10} \times 1531 = 765.5$ or 766.
9. log tan 82° 51' = 10.90156 − 10. $\frac{1}{10} \times 1033 = 103.3$ or 103.
10. log tan 36° 28' = 9.86868 − 10. $\frac{8}{10} \times 265 = 212.$

2. Find   log cos 54° 44'.

The given angle is between 54° 40' and 54° 50'.

log cos 54° 50' = 9.76039 − 10

log cos 54° 44'   10' = 9.76146 − 10 $T = 179$

$m = 4'$

log cos 54° 40' = 9.76218 − 10

Note: The lower logarithm in the above form is the *first* logarithm met as you read up (or down) the cosine column.

If 10' make a difference of 179 in the table, then 4' will make a difference of $\frac{4}{10}$ of 179 in the table. $\frac{4}{10}$ of 179 = 71.6 or 72.

Subtract .00072 from the log cos 54° 40'.

EXPLANATION OF EXPANDED TABLES

If m is the number of minutes for which interpolation is made, then the correction to be *subtracted* is

$$\frac{m}{10} \times T.$$

The same method is used in finding the "log cot."

EXERCISES

Verify the following logarithms.

1. $\log \cos 22° \ 15' = 9.96639 - 10.$ $\quad \frac{5}{10} \times 51 = 25.5$ or 26.
2. $\log \cos 55° \ 16' = 9.75569 - 10.$ $\quad \frac{6}{10} \times 182 = 109.2$ or 109.
3. $\log \cos 6° \ 47' = 9.99694 - 10.$ $\quad \frac{7}{10} \times 15 = 10.5$ or 11.
4. $\log \cos 87° \ 22' = 8.66209 - 10.$ $\quad \frac{2}{10} \times 2801 = 560.2$ or 560.
5. $\log \cot 14° \ 48' = 10.57806 - 10.$ $\quad \frac{8}{10} \times 513 = 410.4$ or 410.
6. $\log \cot 53° \ 14' = 9.87343 - 10.$ $\quad \frac{4}{10} \times 263 = 105.2$ or 105.
7. $\log \cot 4° \ 18' = 11.12389 - 10.$ $\quad \frac{8}{10} \times 1710 = 1368.$
8. $\log \cot 63° \ 55' = 9.68978 - 10.$ $\quad \frac{5}{10} \times 320 = 160.$
9. $\log \cos 36° \ 52' = 9.90311 - 10.$ $\quad \frac{2}{10} \times 95 = 19.$
10. $\log \cot 20° \ 44' = 10.42190 - 10.$ $\quad \frac{4}{10} \times 381 = 152.4$ or 152.
11. $\log \cos 72° \ 27' = 9.47934 - 10.$ $\quad \frac{7}{10} \times 399 = 279.3$ or 279.
12. $\log \cot 3° \ 49' = 11.17584 - 10.$ $\quad \frac{9}{10} \times 1936 = 1742.4$ or 1742.

8. How to find the angle corresponding to a given logarithm of a function

EXAMPLES

1. Given $\log \sin A = 9.63493 - 10$; find angle A.

Reading down the sine column, we observe that $9.63493 - 10$ is between $9.63398 - 10$ and $9.63662 - 10$.

$\log \sin 25° \ 40' \quad\quad\quad\quad = 9.63662 - 10$

$\log \sin A \ (25° \ 34') \quad 10' \quad = 9.63493 - 10 \quad T = 264$

$\quad\quad\quad\quad\quad\quad\quad\quad\quad\quad t = 95$

$\log \sin 25° \ 30' \quad\quad\quad\quad = 9.63398 - 10$

If a difference of 264 in the table makes a difference of 10' in the angle, then a difference of 95 will make a difference of $\frac{95}{264}$ of 10' in the angle. $\frac{95}{264}$ of $10' = 3.6'$ or $4'$. *Add* 4' to $25° \ 30'$. $A = 25° \ 34'$.

The *additive correction* in minutes is expressed by

$$\frac{t}{T} \times 10'.$$

The same method is used in finding the angle from the "log tan."

EXERCISES

Verify the following.

1. $\log \sin A = 9.46342 - 10.$ $A = 16° 54'.$ $\frac{164}{416} \times 10' = 4'.$
2. $\log \sin A = 9.95168 - 10.$ $A = 63° 28'.$ $\frac{52}{63} \times 10' = 8'.$
3. $\log \sin A = 8.90000 - 10.$ $A = 4° 33'.$ $\frac{536}{1576} \times 10' = 3'.$
4. $\log \tan A = 9.65002 - 10.$ $A = 24° 4'.$ $\frac{144}{339} \times 10' = 4'.$
5. $\log \tan A = 10.46946 - 10.$ $A = 71° 16'.$ $\frac{231}{415} \times 10' = 6'.$
6. $\log \tan A = 8.97827 - 10.$ $A = 5° 26'.$ $\frac{814}{1345} \times 10' = 6'.$

2. Given $\log \cos A = 9.67756 - 10$; find angle A.

Reading up the column having "Cos A" at the bottom, we observe that $9.67756 - 10$ is between $9.67866 - 10$ and $9.67633 - 10$.

$\log \cos 61° 40' = 9.67633 - 10$

$\log \cos A\ (61° 35')\quad 10' \quad = 9.67756 - 10 \quad T = 233$

$\qquad\qquad\qquad\qquad\qquad t = 110$

$\log \cos 61° 30' = 9.67866 - 10$

Note: The lower logarithm in the above form is the *first* logarithm met as you read up (or down) the cosine column.

If a difference of 233 in the table makes a difference of 10′ in the angle, then a difference of 110 will make a difference of $\frac{110}{233}$ of 10′ in the angle. $\frac{110}{233}$ of $10' = 5'$. *Add* 5′ to 61° 30′. $A = 61° 35'$.

The *additive correction* in minutes is expressed by

$$\frac{t}{T} \times 10'.$$

The same method is used in finding the angle from the "log cot."

EXERCISES

Verify the following.

1. $\log \cos A = 9.78475 - 10.$ $A = 52° 28'.$ $\frac{134}{164} \times 10' = 8'.$
2. $\log \cos A = 9.87416 - 10.$ $A = 41° 33'.$ $\frac{30}{112} \times 10' = 3'.$
3. $\log \cos A = 9.66640 - 10.$ $A = 62° 22'.$ $\frac{42}{241} \times 10' = 2'.$
4. $\log \cos A = 8.91500 - 10.$ $A = 85° 17'.$ $\frac{1061}{1521} \times 10' = 7'.$
5. $\log \cot A = 9.61234 - 10.$ $A = 67° 44'.$ $\frac{130}{360} \times 10' = 4'.$
6. $\log \cot A = 10.48225 - 10.$ $A = 18° 14'.$ $\frac{169}{425} \times 10' = 4'.$
7. $\log \cot A = 9.88024 - 10.$ $A = 52° 48'.$ $\frac{212}{262} \times 10' = 8'.$
8. $\log \cot A = 8.90608 - 10.$ $A = 85° 24'.$ $\frac{577}{1587} \times 10' = 4'.$
9. $\log \cos A = 9.16482 - 10.$ $A = 81° 36'.$ $\frac{488}{854} \times 10' = 6'.$
10. $\log \cot A = 10.26302 - 10.$ $A = 28° 37'.$ $\frac{222}{301} \times 10' = 7'.$
11. $\log \cos A = 9.60010 - 10.$ $A = 66° 32'.$ $\frac{60}{292} \times 10' = 2'.$

EXPANDED TABLES

Table IV. Natural Trigonometric Functions

Angle	Sin A	Tan A	Cot A	Cos A		
0° 00'	0.0000	0.0000	—	1.0000	90°	00'
10	.0029	.0029	343.77	1.0000		50
20	.0058	.0058	171.89	1.0000		40
30	.0087	.0087	114.59	1.0000		30
40	.0116	.0116	85.940	.9999		20
50	.0145	.0145	68.750	.9999		10
1° 00'	.0175	.0175	57.290	.9998	89°	00'
10	.0204	.0204	49.104	.9998		50
20	.0233	.0233	42.964	.9997		40
30	.0262	.0262	38.188	.9997		30
40	.0291	.0291	34.368	.9996		20
50	.0320	.0320	31.242	.9995		10
2° 00'	.0349	.0349	28.636	.9994	88°	00'
10	.0378	.0378	26.432	.9993		50
20	.0407	.0407	24.542	.9992		40
30	.0436	.0437	22.904	.9990		30
40	.0465	.0466	21.470	.9989		20
50	.0494	.0495	20.206	.9988		10
3° 00'	.0523	.0524	19.081	.9986	87°	00'
10	.0552	.0553	18.075	.9985		50
20	.0581	.0582	17.169	.9983		40
30	.0610	.0612	16.350	.9981		30
40	.0640	.0641	15.605	.9980		20
50	.0669	.0670	14.924	.9978		10
4° 00'	.0698	.0699	14.301	.9976	86°	00'
10	.0727	.0729	13.727	.9974		50
20	.0756	.0758	13.197	.9971		40
30	.0785	.0787	12.706	.9969		30
40	.0814	.0816	12.251	.9967		20
50	.0843	.0846	11.826	.9964		10
5° 00'	.0872	.0875	11.430	.9962	85°	00'
10	.0901	.0904	11.059	.9959		50
20	.0929	.0934	10.712	.9957		40
30	.0958	.0963	10.385	.9954		30
40	.0987	.0992	10.078	.9951		20
50	.1016	.1022	9.7882	.9948		10
6° 00'	.1045	.1051	9.5144	.9945	84°	00'
10	.1074	.1080	9.2553	.9942		50
20	.1103	.1110	9.0098	.9939		40
30	.1132	.1139	8.7769	.9936		30
40	.1161	.1169	8.5555	.9932		20
50	.1190	.1198	8.3450	.9929		10
7° 00'	.1219	.1228	8.1443	.9925	83°	00'
10	.1248	.1257	7.9530	.9922		50
20	.1276	.1287	7.7704	.9918		40
30	.1305	.1317	7.5958	.9914		30
40	.1334	.1346	7.4287	.9911		20
50	.1363	.1376	7.2687	.9907		10
8° 00'	.1392	.1405	7.1154	.9903	82°	00'
10	.1421	.1435	6.9682	.9899		50
20	.1449	.1465	6.8269	.9894		40
30	.1478	.1495	6.6912	.9890		30
40	.1507	.1524	6.5606	.9886		20
50	.1536	.1554	6.4348	.9881		10
9° 00'	.1564	.1584	6.3138	.9877	81°	00'
	Cos A	Cot A	Tan A	Sin A	Angle	

Table IV. Natural Trigonometric Functions—Continued

Angle	Sin A	Tan A	Cot A	Cos A		
9° 00'	.1564	.1584	6.3138	.9877	81°	00'
10	.1593	.1614	6.1970	.9872		50
20	.1622	.1644	6.0844	.9868		40
30	.1650	.1673	5.9758	.9863		30
40	.1679	.1703	5.8708	.9858		20
50	.1708	.1733	5.7694	.9853		10
10° 00'	.1736	.1763	5.6713	.9848	80°	00'
10	.1765	.1793	5.5764	.9843		50
20	.1794	.1823	5.4845	.9838		40
30	.1822	.1853	5.3955	.9833		30
40	.1851	.1883	5.3093	.9827		20
50	.1880	.1914	5.2257	.9822		10
11° 00'	.1908	.1944	5.1446	.9816	79°	00'
10	.1937	.1974	5.0658	.9811		50
20	.1965	.2004	4.9894	.9805		40
30	.1994	.2035	4.9152	.9799		30
40	.2022	.2065	4.8430	.9793		20
50	.2051	.2095	4.7729	.9787		10
12° 00'	.2079	.2126	4.7046	.9781	78°	00'
10	.2108	.2156	4.6382	.9775		50
20	.2136	.2186	4.5736	.9769		40
30	.2164	.2217	4.5107	.9763		30
40	.2193	.2247	4.4494	.9757		20
50	.2221	.2278	4.3897	.9750		10
13° 00'	.2250	.2309	4.3315	.9744	77°	00'
10	.2278	.2339	4.2747	.9737		50
20	.2306	.2370	4.2193	.9730		40
30	.2334	.2401	4.1653	.9724		30
40	.2363	.2432	4.1126	.9717		20
50	.2391	.2462	4.0611	.9710		10
14° 00'	.2419	.2493	4.0108	.9703	76°	00'
10	.2447	.2524	3.9617	.9696		50
20	.2476	.2555	3.9136	.9689		40
30	.2504	.2586	3.8667	.9681		30
40	.2532	.2617	3.8208	.9674		20
50	.2560	.2648	3.7760	.9667		10
15° 00'	.2588	.2679	3.7321	.9659	75°	00'
10	.2616	.2711	3.6891	.9652		50
20	.2644	.2742	3.6470	.9644		40
30	.2672	.2773	3.6059	.9636		30
40	.2700	.2805	3.5656	.9628		20
50	.2728	.2836	3.5261	.9621		10
16° 00'	.2756	.2867	3.4874	.9613	74°	00'
10	.2784	.2899	3.4495	.9605		50
20	.2812	.2931	3.4124	.9596		40
30	.2840	.2962	3.3759	.9588		30
40	.2868	.2994	3.3402	.9580		20
50	.2896	.3026	3.3052	.9572		10
17° 00'	.2924	.3057	3.2709	.9563	73°	00'
10	.2952	.3089	3.2371	.9555		50
20	.2979	.3121	3.2041	.9546		40
30	.3007	.3153	3.1716	.9537		30
40	.3035	.3185	3.1397	.9528		20
50	.3062	.3217	3.1084	.9520		10
18° 00'	.3090	.3249	3.0777	.9511	72°	00'
	Cos A	Cot A	Tan A	Sin A	Angle	

EXPANDED TABLES

Table IV. Natural Trigonometric Functions—Continued

Angle		Sin A	Tan A	Cot A	Cos A		
18°	00'	.3090	.3249	3.0777	.9511	72°	00'
	10	.3118	.3281	3.0475	.9502		50
	20	.3145	.3314	3.0178	.9492		40
	30	.3173	.3346	2.9887	.9483		30
	40	.3201	.3378	2.9600	.9474		20
	50	.3228	.3411	2.9319	.9465		10
19°	00'	.3256	.3443	2.9042	.9455	71°	00'
	10	.3283	.3476	2.8770	.9446		50
	20	.3311	.3508	2.8502	.9436		40
	30	.3338	.3541	2.8239	.9426		30
	40	.3365	.3574	2.7980	.9417		20
	50	.3393	.3607	2.7725	.9407		10
20°	00'	.3420	.3640	2.7475	.9397	70°	00'
	10	.3448	.3673	2.7228	.9387		50
	20	.3475	.3706	2.6985	.9377		40
	30	.3502	.3739	2.6746	.9367		30
	40	.3529	.3772	2.6511	.9356		20
	50	.3557	.3805	2.6279	.9346		10
21°	00'	.3584	.3839	2.6051	.9336	69°	00'
	10	.3611	.3872	2.5826	.9325		50
	20	.3638	.3906	2.5605	.9315		40
	30	.3665	.3939	2.5386	.9304		30
	40	.3692	.3973	2.5172	.9293		20
	50	.3719	.4006	2.4960	.9283		10
22°	00'	.3746	.4040	2.4751	.9272	68°	00'
	10	.3773	.4074	2.4545	.9261		50
	20	.3800	.4108	2.4342	.9250		40
	30	.3827	.4142	2.4142	.9239		30
	40	.3854	.4176	2.3945	.9228		20
	50	.3881	.4210	2.3750	.9216		10
23°	00'	.3907	.4245	2.3559	.9205	67°	00'
	10	.3934	.4279	2.3369	.9194		50
	20	.3961	.4314	2.3183	.9182		40
	30	.3987	.4348	2.2998	.9171		30
	40	.4014	.4383	2.2817	.9159		20
	50	.4041	.4417	2.2637	.9147		10
24°	00'	.4067	.4452	2.2460	.9135	66°	00'
	10	.4094	.4487	2.2286	.9124		50
	20	.4120	.4522	2.2113	.9112		40
	30	.4147	.4557	2.1943	.9100		30
	40	.4173	.4592	2.1775	.9088		20
	50	.4200	.4628	2.1609	.9075		10
25°	00'	.4226	.4663	2.1445	.9063	65°	00'
	10	.4253	.4699	2.1283	.9051		50
	20	.4279	.4734	2.1123	.9038		40
	30	.4305	.4770	2.0965	.9026		30
	40	.4331	.4806	2.0809	.9013		20
	50	.4358	.4841	2.0655	.9001		10
26°	00'	.4384	.4877	2.0503	.8988	64°	00'
	10	.4410	.4913	2.0353	.8975		50
	20	.4436	.4950	2.0204	.8962		40
	30	.4462	.4986	2.0057	.8949		30
	40	.4488	.5022	1.9912	.8936		20
	50	.4514	.5059	1.9768	.8923		10
27°	00'	.4540	.5095	1.9626	.8910	63°	00'
		Cos A	Cot A	Tan A	Sin A	Angle	

Table IV. Natural Trigonometric Functions—Continued

Angle		Sin A	Tan A	Cot A	Cos A		
27°	00'	.4540	.5095	1.9626	.8910	63°	00'
	10	.4566	.5132	1.9486	.8897		50
	20	.4592	.5169	1.9347	.8884		40
	30	.4617	.5206	1.9210	.8870		30
	40	.4643	.5243	1.9074	.8857		20
	50	.4669	.5280	1.8940	.8843		10
28°	00'	.4695	.5317	1.8807	.8829	62°	00'
	10	.4720	.5354	1.8676	.8816		50
	20	.4746	.5392	1.8546	.8802		40
	30	.4772	.5430	1.8418	.8788		30
	40	.4797	.5467	1.8291	.8774		20
	50	.4823	.5505	1.8165	.8760		10
29°	00'	.4848	.5543	1.8040	.8746	61°	00'
	10	.4874	.5581	1.7917	.8732		50
	20	.4899	.5619	1.7796	.8718		40
	30	.4924	.5658	1.7675	.8704		30
	40	.4950	.5696	1.7556	.8689		20
	50	.4975	.5735	1.7437	.8675		10
30°	00'	.5000	.5774	1.7321	.8660	60°	00'
	10	.5025	.5812	1.7205	.8646		50
	20	.5050	.5851	1.7090	.8631		40
	30	.5075	.5890	1.6977	.8616		30
	40	.5100	.5930	1.6864	.8601		20
	50	.5125	.5969	1.6753	.8587		10
31°	00'	.5150	.6009	1.6643	.8572	59°	00'
	10	.5175	.6048	1.6534	.8557		50
	20	.5200	.6088	1.6426	.8542		40
	30	.5225	.6128	1.6319	.8526		30
	40	.5250	.6168	1.6212	.8511		20
	50	.5275	.6208	1.6107	.8496		10
32°	00'	.5299	.6249	1.6003	.8480	58°	00'
	10	.5324	.6289	1.5900	.8465		50
	20	.5348	.6330	1.5798	.8450		40
	30	.5373	.6371	1.5697	.8434		30
	40	.5398	.6412	1.5597	.8418		20
	50	.5422	.6453	1.5497	.8403		10
33°	00'	.5446	.6494	1.5399	.8387	57°	00'
	10	.5471	.6536	1.5301	.8371		50
	20	.5495	.6577	1.5204	.8355		40
	30	.5519	.6619	1.5108	.8339		30
	40	.5544	.6661	1.5013	.8323		20
	50	.5568	.6703	1.4919	.8307		10
34°	00'	.5592	.6745	1.4826	.8290	56°	00'
	10	.5616	.6787	1.4733	.8274		50
	20	.5640	.6830	1.4641	.8258		40
	30	.5664	.6873	1.4550	.8241		30
	40	.5688	.6916	1.4460	.8225		20
	50	.5712	.6959	1.4370	.8208		10
35°	00'	.5736	.7002	1.4281	.8192	55°	00'
	10	.5760	.7046	1.4193	.8175		50
	20	.5783	.7089	1.4106	.8158		40
	30	.5807	.7133	1.4019	.8141		30
	40	.5831	.7177	1.3934	.8124		20
	50	.5854	.7221	1.3848	.8107		10
36°	00'	.5878	.7265	1.3764	.8090	54°	00'
		Cos A	Cot A	Tan A	Sin A	Angle	

EXPANDED TABLES

Table IV. Natural Trigonometric Functions—Continued

Angle		Sin A	Tan A	Cot A	Cos A		
36°	00'	.5878	.7265	1.3764	.8090	54°	00'
	10	.5901	.7310	1.3680	.8073		50
	20	.5925	.7355	1.3597	.8056		40
	30	.5948	.7400	1.3514	.8039		30
	40	.5972	.7445	1.3432	.8021		20
	50	.5995	.7490	1.3351	.8004		10
37°	00'	.6018	.7536	1.3270	.7986	53°	00'
	10	.6041	.7581	1.3190	.7969		50
	20	.6065	.7627	1.3111	.7951		40
	30	.6088	.7673	1.3032	.7934		30
	40	.6111	.7720	1.2954	.7916		20
	50	.6134	.7766	1.2876	.7898		10
38°	00'	.6157	.7813	1.2799	.7880	52°	00'
	10	.6180	.7860	1.2723	.7862		50
	20	.6202	.7907	1.2647	.7844		40
	30	.6225	.7954	1.2572	.7826		30
	40	.6248	.8002	1.2497	.7808		20
	50	.6271	.8050	1.2423	.7790		10
39°	00'	.6293	.8098	1.2349	.7771	51°	00'
	10	.6316	.8146	1.2276	.7753		50
	20	.6338	.8195	1.2203	.7735		40
	30	.6361	.8243	1.2131	.7716		30
	40	.6383	.8292	1.2059	.7698		20
	50	.6406	.8342	1.1988	.7679		10
40°	00'	.6428	.8391	1.1918	.7660	50°	00'
	10	.6450	.8441	1.1847	.7642		50
	20	.6472	.8491	1.1778	.7623		40
	30	.6494	.8541	1.1708	.7604		30
	40	.6517	.8591	1.1640	.7585		20
	50	.6539	.8642	1.1571	.7566		10
41°	00'	.6561	.8693	1.1504	.7547	49°	00'
	10	.6583	.8744	1.1436	.7528		50
	20	.6604	.8796	1.1369	.7509		40
	30	.6626	.8847	1.1303	.7490		30
	40	.6648	.8899	1.1237	.7470		20
	50	.6670	.8952	1.1171	.7451		10
42°	00'	.6691	.9004	1.1106	.7431	48°	00'
	10	.6713	.9057	1.1041	.7412		50
	20	.6734	.9110	1.0977	.7392		40
	30	.6756	.9163	1.0913	.7373		30
	40	.6777	.9217	1.0850	.7353		20
	50	.6799	.9271	1.0786	.7333		10
43°	00'	.6820	.9325	1.0724	.7314	47°	00'
	10	.6841	.9380	1.0661	.7294		50
	20	.6862	.9435	1.0599	.7274		40
	30	.6884	.9490	1.0538	.7254		30
	40	.6905	.9545	1.0477	.7234		20
	50	.6926	.9601	1.0416	.7214		10
44°	00'	.6947	.9657	1.0355	.7193	46°	00'
	10	.6967	.9713	1.0295	.7173		50
	20	.6988	.9770	1.0235	.7153		40
	30	.7009	.9827	1.0176	.7133		30
	40	.7030	.9884	1.0117	.7112		20
	50	.7050	.9942	1.0058	.7092		10
45°	00'	.7071	1.0000	1.0000	.7071	45°	00'
		Cos A	Cot A	Tan A	Sin A	Angle	

Table V. Logarithms of Numbers*

N	0	1	2	3	4	5	6	7	8	9
10	00000	00432	00860	01284	01703	02119	02531	02938	03342	03743
11	04139	04532	04922	05308	05690	06070	06446	06819	07188	07555
12	07918	08279	08636	08991	09342	09691	10037	10380	10721	11059
13	11394	11727	12057	12385	12710	13033	13354	13672	13988	14301
14	14613	14922	15229	15534	15836	16137	16435	16732	17026	17319
15	17609	17898	18184	18469	18752	19033	19312	19590	19866	20140
16	20412	20683	20952	21219	21484	21748	22011	22272	22531	22789
17	23045	23300	23553	23805	24055	24304	24551	24797	25042	25285
18	25527	25768	26007	26245	26482	26717	26951	27184	27416	27646
19	27875	28103	28330	28556	28780	29003	29226	29447	29667	29885
20	30103	30320	30535	30750	30963	31175	31387	31597	31806	32015
21	32222	32428	32634	32838	33041	33244	33445	33646	33846	34044
22	34242	34439	34635	34830	35024	35218	35411	35603	35793	35984
23	36173	36361	36549	36736	36922	37107	37291	37475	37658	37840
24	38021	38202	38382	38561	38739	38917	39094	39270	39445	39620
25	39794	39967	40140	40312	40483	40654	40824	40993	41162	41330
26	41497	41664	41830	41996	42160	42325	42488	42651	42813	42975
27	43136	43297	43457	43616	43775	43933	44091	44248	44404	44560
28	44716	44871	45025	45179	45332	45484	45637	45788	45939	46090
29	46240	46389	46538	46687	46835	46982	47129	47276	47422	47567
30	47712	47857	48001	48144	48287	48430	48572	48714	48855	48996
31	49136	49276	49415	49554	49693	49831	49969	50106	50243	50379
32	50515	50651	50786	50920	51055	51188	51322	51445	51587	51720
33	51851	51983	52114	52244	52375	52504	52634	52763	52892	53020
34	53148	53275	53403	53529	53656	53782	53908	54033	54158	54283
35	54407	54531	54654	54777	54900	55023	55145	55267	55388	55509
36	55630	55751	55871	55991	56110	56229	56348	56467	56585	56703
37	56820	56937	57054	57171	57287	57403	57519	57634	57749	57864
38	57978	58092	58206	58320	58433	58546	58659	58771	58883	58995
39	59106	59218	59329	59439	59550	59660	59770	59879	59988	60097
40	60206	60314	60423	60531	60638	60746	60853	60959	61066	61172
41	61278	61384	61490	61595	61700	61805	61909	62014	62118	62221
42	62325	62428	62531	62634	62737	62839	62941	63043	63144	63246
43	63347	63448	63548	63649	63749	63849	63949	64048	64147	64246
44	64345	64444	64542	64640	64738	64836	64933	65031	65128	65225
45	65321	65418	65514	65610	65706	65801	65896	65992	66087	66181
46	66276	66370	66464	66558	66652	66745	66839	66932	67025	67117
47	67210	67302	67394	67486	67578	67669	67761	67852	67943	68034
48	68124	68215	68305	68395	68485	68574	68664	68753	68842	68931
49	69020	69108	69197	69285	69373	69461	69548	69636	69723	69810
50	69897	69984	70070	70157	70243	70329	70415	70501	70586	70672
51	70757	70842	70927	71012	71096	71181	71265	71349	71433	71517
52	71600	71684	71767	71850	71933	72016	72099	72181	72263	72346
53	72428	72509	72591	72673	72754	72835	72916	72997	73078	73159
54	73239	73320	73400	73480	73560	73640	73719	73799	73878	73957

*This table gives the mantissas of numbers with the decimal point omitted. Characteristics are determined by inspection from the numbers.

EXPANDED TABLES

Table V. Logarithms of Numbers—Continued*

N	0	1	2	3	4	5	6	7	8	9
55	74036	74115	74194	74273	74351	74429	74507	74586	74663	74741
56	74819	74896	74974	75051	75128	75205	75282	75358	75435	75511
57	75587	75664	75740	75815	75891	75967	76042	76118	76193	76268
58	76343	76418	76492	76567	76641	76716	76790	76864	76938	77012
59	77085	77159	77232	77305	77379	77452	77525	77597	77670	77743
60	77815	77887	77960	78032	78104	78176	78247	78319	78390	78462
61	78533	78604	78675	78746	78817	78888	78958	79029	79099	79169
62	79239	79309	79379	79449	79518	79588	79657	79727	79796	79865
63	79934	80003	80072	80140	80209	80277	80346	80414	80482	80550
64	80618	80686	80754	80821	80889	80956	81023	81090	81158	81224
65	81291	81358	81425	81491	81558	81624	81690	81757	81823	81889
66	81954	82020	82086	82151	82217	82282	82347	82413	82478	82543
67	82607	82672	82737	82802	82866	82930	82995	83059	83123	83187
68	83251	83315	83378	83442	83506	83569	83632	83696	83759	83822
69	83885	83948	84011	84073	84136	84198	84261	84323	84386	84448
70	84510	84572	84634	84696	84757	84819	84880	84942	85003	85065
71	85126	85187	85248	85309	85370	85431	85491	85552	85612	85673
72	85733	85794	85854	85914	85974	86034	86094	86153	86213	86273
73	86332	86392	86451	86510	86570	86629	86688	86747	86806	86864
74	86923	86982	87040	87099	87157	87216	87274	87332	87390	87448
75	87506	87564	87622	87679	87737	87795	87852	87910	87967	88024
76	88081	88138	88195	88252	88309	88366	88423	88480	88536	88593
77	88649	88705	88762	88818	88874	88930	88986	89042	89098	89154
78	89209	89265	89321	89376	89432	89487	89542	89597	89653	89708
79	89763	89818	89873	89927	89982	90037	90091	90146	90200	90255
80	90309	90363	90417	90472	90526	90580	90634	90687	90741	90795
81	90849	90902	90956	91009	91062	91116	91169	91222	91275	91328
82	91381	91434	91487	91540	91593	91645	91698	91751	91803	91855
83	91908	91960	92012	92065	92117	92169	92221	92273	92324	92376
84	92428	92480	92531	92583	92634	92686	92737	92788	92840	92891
85	92942	92993	93044	93095	93146	93197	93247	93298	93349	93399
86	93450	93500	93551	93601	93651	93702	93752	93802	93852	93902
87	93952	94002	94052	94101	94151	94201	94250	94300	94349	94399
88	94448	94498	94547	94596	94645	94694	94743	94792	94841	94890
89	94939	94988	95036	95085	95134	95182	95231	95279	95328	95376
90	95424	95472	95521	95569	95617	95665	95713	95761	95809	95856
91	95904	95952	95999	96047	96095	96142	96190	96237	96284	96332
92	96379	96426	96473	96520	96567	96614	96661	96708	96755	96802
93	96848	96895	96942	96988	97035	97081	97128	97174	97220	97267
94	97313	97359	97405	97451	97497	97543	97589	97635	97681	97727
95	97772	97818	97864	97909	97955	98000	98046	98091	98137	98182
96	98227	98272	98318	98363	98408	98453	98498	98543	98588	98632
97	98677	98722	98767	98811	98856	98900	98945	98989	99034	99078
98	99123	99167	99211	99255	99300	99344	99388	99432	99476	99520
99	99564	99607	99651	99695	99739	99782	99826	99870	99913	99957

*This table gives the mantissas of numbers with the decimal point omitted. Characteristics are determined by inspection from the numbers.

Table VI. Logarithms of Trigonometric Functions*

Angle	Log Sin	Log Tan	Log Cot	Log Cos	
0° 00'	—	—	—	10.00000	90° 00'
10	7.46373	7.46373	12.53627	10.00000	50
20	7.76475	7.76476	12.23524	9.99999	40
30	7.94084	7.94086	12.05914	9.99998	30
40	8.06578	8.06581	11.93419	9.99997	20
50	8.16268	8.16273	11.83727	9.99995	10
1° 00'	8.24186	8.24192	11.75808	9.99993	89° 00'
10	8.30879	8.30888	11.69112	9.99991	50
20	8.36678	8.36689	11.63311	9.99988	40
30	8.41792	8.41807	11.58193	9.99985	30
40	8.46366	8.46384	11.53615	9.99982	20
50	8.50504	8.50527	11.49473	9.99978	10
2° 00'	8.54282	8.54308	11.45692	9.99974	88° 00'
10	8.57757	8.57788	11.42212	9.99969	50
20	8.60973	8.61009	11.38991	9.99964	40
30	8.63968	8.64009	11.35991	9.99959	30
40	8.66769	8.66816	11.33184	9.99953	20
50	8.69400	8.69453	11.30547	9.99947	10
3° 00'	8.71880	8.71940	11.28060	9.99940	87° 00'
10	8.74226	8.74292	11.25708	9.99934	50
20	8.76451	8.76525	11.23475	9.99926	40
30	8.78568	8.78649	11.21351	9.99919	30
40	8.80585	8.80674	11.19326	9.99911	20
50	8.82513	8.82610	11.17390	9.99903	10
4° 00'	8.84358	8.84464	11.15536	9.99894	86° 00'
10	8.86128	8.86243	11.13757	9.99885	50
20	8.87829	8.87953	11.12047	9.99876	40
30	8.89464	8.89598	11.10402	9.99866	30
40	8.91040	8.91185	11.08815	9.99856	20
50	8.92561	8.92716	11.07284	9.99845	10
5° 00'	8.94030	8.94195	11.05805	9.99834	85° 00'
10	8.95450	8.95627	11.04373	9.99823	50
20	8.96825	8.97013	11.02987	9.99812	40
30	8.98157	8.98358	11.01642	9.99800	30
40	8.99450	8.99662	11.00338	9.99787	20
50	9.00704	9.00930	10.99070	9.99775	10
6° 00'	9.01923	9.02162	10.97838	9.99761	84° 00'
10	9.03109	9.03361	10.96639	9.99748	50
20	9.04262	9.04528	10.95472	9.99734	40
30	9.05386	9.05666	10.94334	9.99720	30
40	9.06481	9.06775	10.93224	9.99705	20
50	9.07548	9.07858	10.92142	9.99690	10
7° 00'	9.08589	9.08914	10.91086	9.99675	83° 00'
10	9.09606	9.09947	10.90053	9.99659	50
20	9.10599	9.10956	10.89044	9.99643	40
30	9.11570	9.11943	10.88057	9.99627	30
40	9.12519	9.12909	10.87091	9.99610	20
50	9.13447	9.13854	10.86146	9.99593	10
8° 00'	9.14356	9.14780	10.85220	9.99575	82° 00'
10	9.15245	9.15688	10.84312	9.99557	50
20	9.16116	9.16577	10.83423	9.99539	40
30	9.16970	9.17450	10.82550	9.99520	30
40	9.17807	9.18306	10.81694	9.99501	20
50	9.18628	9.19146	10.80854	9.99482	10
9° 00'	9.19433	9.19971	10.80029	9.99462	81° 00'
	Log Cos	Log Cot	Log Tan	Log Sin	Angle

*These tables give the logarithms increased by 10. Hence in each case 10 should be subtracted.

Table VI. Logarithms of Trigonometric Functions—Continued

Angle		Log Sin	Log Tan	Log Cot	Log Cos		
9°	00'	9.19433	9.19971	10.80029	9.99462	81°	00'
	10	9.20223	9.20782	10.79218	9.99442		50
	20	9.20999	9.21578	10.78422	9.99421		40
	30	9.21761	9.22361	10.77639	9.99400		30
	40	9.22509	9.23130	10.76870	9.99379		20
	50	9.23244	9.23887	10.76113	9.99357		10
10°	00'	9.23967	9.24632	10.75368	9.99335	80°	00'
	10	9.24677	9.25365	10.74635	9.99313		50
	20	9.25376	9.26086	10.73914	9.99290		40
	30	9.26063	9.26797	10.73203	9.99267		30
	40	9.26739	9.27496	10.72504	9.99243		20
	50	9.27405	9.28186	10.71814	9.99219		10
11°	00'	9.28060	9.28865	10.71135	9.99195	79°	00'
	10	9.28705	9.29535	10.70465	9.99170		50
	20	9.29340	9.30195	10.69805	9.99145		40
	30	9.29966	9.30846	10.69154	9.99119		30
	40	9.30582	9.31489	10.68511	9.99093		20
	50	9.31189	9.32122	10.67878	9.99067		10
12°	00'	9.31788	9.32747	10.67253	9.99040	78°	00'
	10	9.32378	9.33365	10.66635	9.99013		50
	20	9.32960	9.33974	10.66026	9.98986		40
	30	9.33534	9.34576	10.65424	9.98958		30
	40	9.34100	9.35170	10.64830	9.98930		20
	50	9.34658	9.35757	10.64243	9.98901		10
13°	00'	9.35209	9.36336	10.63664	9.98872	77°	00'
	10	9.35752	9.36909	10.63091	9.98843		50
	20	9.36289	9.37476	10.62524	9.98813		40
	30	9.36819	9.38035	10.61965	9.98783		30
	40	9.37341	9.38589	10.61411	9.98753		20
	50	9.37858	9.39136	10.60864	9.98722		10
14°	00'	9.38368	9.39677	10.60323	9.98690	76°	00'
	10	9.38871	9.40212	10.59788	9.98659		50
	20	9.39369	9.40742	10.59258	9.98627		40
	30	9.39860	9.41266	10.58734	9.98594		30
	40	9.40346	9.41784	10.58216	9.98561		20
	50	9.40825	9.42297	10.57703	9.98528		10
15°	00'	9.41300	9.42805	10.57195	9.98494	75°	00'
	10	9.41768	9.43308	10.56692	9.98460		50
	20	9.42232	9.43806	10.56194	9.98426		40
	30	9.42690	9.44299	10.55701	9.98391		30
	40	9.43143	9.44787	10.55213	9.98356		20
	50	9.43591	9.45271	10.54729	9.98320		10
16°	00'	9.44034	9.45750	10.54250	9.98284	74°	00'
	10	9.44472	9.46224	10.53776	9.98248		50
	20	9.44905	9.46694	10.53306	9.98211		40
	30	9.45334	9.47160	10.52840	9.98174		30
	40	9.45758	9.47622	10.52378	9.98136		20
	50	9.46178	9.48080	10.51920	9.98098		10
17°	00'	9.46594	9.48534	10.51466	9.98060	73°	00'
	10	9.47005	9.48984	10.51016	9.98021		50
	20	9.47411	9.49430	10.50570	9.97982		40
	30	9.47814	9.49872	10.50128	9.97942		30
	40	9.48213	9.50311	10.49689	9.97902		20
	50	9.48607	9.50746	10.49254	9.97861		10
18°	00'	9.48998	9.51178	10.48822	9.97821	72°	00'
		Log Cos	Log Cot	Log Tan	Log Sin	Angle	

Table VI. Logarithms of Trigonometric Functions—Continued

Angle		Log Sin	Log Tan	Log Cot	Log Cos		
18°	00'	9.48998	9.51178	10.48822	9.97821	72°	00'
	10	9.49385	9.51606	10.48394	9.97779		50
	20	9.49768	9.52031	10.47969	9.97738		40
	30	9.50148	9.52452	10.47548	9.97696		30
	40	9.50523	9.52870	10.47130	9.97653		20
	50	9.50896	9.53285	10.46715	9.97610		10
19°	00'	9.51264	9.53697	10.46303	9.97567	71°	00'
	10	9.51629	9.54106	10.45894	9.97523		50
	20	9.51991	9.54512	10.45488	9.97479		40
	30	9.52350	9.54915	10.45085	9.97435		30
	40	9.52705	9.55315	10.44685	9.97390		20
	50	9.53056	9.55712	10.44288	9.97344		10
20°	00'	9.53405	9.56107	10.43893	9.97299	70°	00'
	10	9.53751	9.56498	10.43502	9.97252		50
	20	9.54093	9.56887	10.43113	9.97206		40
	30	9.54433	9.57274	10.42726	9.97159		30
	40	9.54769	9.57658	10.42342	9.97111		20
	50	9.55102	9.58039	10.41961	9.97063		10
21°	00'	9.55433	9.58418	10.41582	9.97015	69°	00'
	10	9.55761	9.58794	10.41206	9.96966		50
	20	9.56085	9.59168	10.40832	9.96917		40
	30	9.56408	9.59540	10.40460	9.96868		30
	40	9.56727	9.59909	10.40091	9.96818		20
	50	9.57044	9.60276	10.39724	9.96767		10
22°	00'	9.57358	9.60641	10.39359	9.96717	68°	00'
	10	9.57669	9.61004	10.38996	9.96665		50
	20	9.57978	9.61364	10.38636	9.96614		40
	30	9.58284	9.61722	10.38278	9.96562		30
	40	9.58588	9.62079	10.37921	9.96509		20
	50	9.58889	9.62433	10.37567	9.96456		10
23°	00'	9.59188	9.62785	10.37215	9.96403	67°	00'
	10	9.59484	9.63135	10.36865	9.96349		50
	20	9.59778	9.63484	10.36516	9.96294		40
	30	9.60070	9.63830	10.36170	9.96240		30
	40	9.60359	9.64175	10.35825	9.96185		20
	50	9.60646	9.64517	10.35483	9.96129		10
24°	00'	9.60931	9.64858	10.35142	9.96073	66°	00'
	10	9.61214	9.65197	10.34803	9.96017		50
	20	9.61494	9.65535	10.34465	9.95960		40
	30	9.61773	9.65870	10.34130	9.95902		30
	40	9.62049	9.66204	10.33796	9.95844		20
	50	9.62323	9.66537	10.33463	9.95786		10
25°	00'	9.62595	9.66867	10.33133	9.95728	65°	00'
	10	9.62865	9.67196	10.32804	9.95668		50
	20	9.63133	9.67524	10.32476	9.95609		40
	30	9.63398	9.67850	10.32150	9.95549		30
	40	9.63662	9.68174	10.31826	9.95488		20
	50	9.63924	9.68497	10.31503	9.95427		10
26°	00'	9.64184	9.68818	10.31182	9.95366	64°	00'
	10	9.64442	9.69138	10.30862	9.95304		50
	20	9.64698	9.69457	10.30543	9.95242		40
	30	9.64953	9.69774	10.30226	9.95179		30
	40	9.65205	9.70089	10.29911	9.95116		20
	50	9.65456	9.70404	10.29596	9.95052		10
27°	00'	9.65705	9.70717	10.29283	9.94988	63°	00'
		Log Cos	Log Cot	Log Tan	Log Sin	Angle	

EXPANDED TABLES

Table VI. Logarithms of Trigonometric Functions—Continued

Angle	Log Sin	Log Tan	Log Cot	Log Cos		
27° 00'	9.65705	9.70717	10.29283	9.94988	63°	00'
10	9.65952	9.71028	10.28972	9.94923		50
20	9.66197	9.71339	10.28661	9.94858		40
30	9.66441	9.71648	10.28352	9.94793		30
40	9.66682	9.71955	10.28045	9.94727		20
50	9.66922	9.72262	10.27738	9.94660		10
28° 00'	9.67161	9.72567	10.27433	9.94593	62°	00'
10	9.67398	9.72872	10.27128	9.94526		50
20	9.67633	9.73175	10.26825	9.94458		40
30	9.67866	9.73476	10.26524	9.94390		30
40	9.68098	9.73777	10.26223	9.94321		20
50	9.68328	9.74077	10.25923	9.94252		10
29° 00'	9.68557	9.74375	10.25625	9.94182	61°	00'
10	9.68784	9.74673	10.25327	9.94112		50
20	9.69010	9.74969	10.25031	9.94041		40
30	9.69234	9.75264	10.24736	9.93970		30
40	9.69456	9.75558	10.24442	9.93898		20
50	9.69677	9.75852	10.24148	9.93826		10
30° 00'	9.69897	9.76144	10.23856	9.93753	60°	00'
10	9.70115	9.76435	10.23565	9.93680		50
20	9.70332	9.76725	10.23275	9.93606		40
30	9.70547	9.77015	10.22985	9.93532		30
40	9.70761	9.77303	10.22697	9.93457		20
50	9.70973	9.77591	10.22409	9.93382		10
31° 00'	9.71184	9.77877	10.22123	9.93307	59°	00'
10	9.71393	9.78163	10.21837	9.93230		50
20	9.71602	9.78448	10.21552	9.93154		40
30	9.71809	9.78732	10.21268	9.93077		30
40	9.72014	9.79015	10.20985	9.92999		20
50	9.72218	9.79297	10.20703	9.92921		10
32° 00'	9.72421	9.79579	10.20421	9.92842	58°	00'
10	9.72622	9.79860	10.20140	9.92763		50
20	9.72823	9.80140	10.19860	9.92683		40
30	9.73022	9.80419	10.19581	9.92603		30
40	9.73219	9.80697	10.19303	9.92522		20
50	9.73416	9.80975	10.19025	9.92441		10
33° 00'	9.73611	9.81252	10.18748	9.92359	57°	00'
10	9.73805	9.81528	10.18472	9.92277		50
20	9.73997	9.81803	10.18197	9.92194		40
30	9.74189	9.82078	10.17922	9.92111		30
40	9.74379	9.82352	10.17648	9.92027		20
50	9.74568	9.82626	10.17374	9.91942		10
34° 00'	9.74756	9.82899	10.17101	9.91857	56°	00'
10	9.74943	9.83171	10.16829	9.91772		50
20	9.75128	9.83442	10.16558	9.91686		40
30	9.75313	9.83713	10.16287	9.91599		30
40	9.75496	9.83984	10.16016	9.91512		20
50	9.75678	9.84254	10.15746	9.91425		10
35° 00'	9.75859	9.84523	10.15477	9.91336	55°	00'
10	9.76039	9.84791	10.15209	9.91248		50
20	9.76218	9.85059	10.14941	9.91158		40
30	9.76395	9.85327	10.14673	9.91069		30
40	9.76572	9.85594	10.14406	9.90978		20
50	9.76747	9.85860	10.14140	9.90887		10
36° 00'	9.76922	9.86126	10.13874	9.90796	54°	00'
	Log Cos	Log Cot	Log Tan	Log Sin	Angle	

Table VI. Logarithms of Trigonometric Functions—Continued

Angle		Log Sin	Log Tan	Log Cot	Log Cos		
36°	00'	9.76922	9.86126	10.13874	9.90796	54°	00'
	10	9.77095	9.86392	10.13608	9.90704		50
	20	9.77268	9.86656	10.13344	9.90611		40
	30	9.77439	9.86921	10.13079	9.90518		30
	40	9.77609	9.87185	10.12815	9.90424		20
	50	9.77778	9.87448	10.12552	9.90330		10
37°	00'	9.77946	9.87711	10.12289	9.90235	53°	00'
	10	9.78113	9.87974	10.12026	9.90139		50
	20	9.78280	9.88236	10.11764	9.90043		40
	30	9.78445	9.88498	10.11502	9.89947		30
	40	9.78609	9.88759	10.11241	9.89849		20
	50	9.78772	9.89020	10.10980	9.89752		10
38°	00'	9.78934	9.89281	10.10719	9.89653	52°	00'
	10	9.79095	9.89541	10.10459	9.89554		50
	20	9.79256	9.89801	10.10199	9.89455		40
	30	9.79415	9.90061	10.09939	9.89354		30
	40	9.79573	9.90320	10.09680	9.89254		20
	50	9.79731	9.90578	10.09422	9.89152		10
39°	00'	9.79887	9.90837	10.09163	9.89050	51°	00'
	10	9.80043	9.91095	10.08905	9.88948		50
	20	9.80197	9.91353	10.08647	9.88844		40
	30	9.80351	9.91610	10.08390	9.88741		30
	40	9.80504	9.91868	10.08132	9.88636		20
	50	9.80656	9.92125	10.07875	9.88531		10
40°	00'	9.80807	9.92381	10.07619	9.88425	50°	00'
	10	9.80957	9.92638	10.07362	9.88319		50
	20	9.81106	9.92894	10.07106	9.88212		40
	30	9.81254	9.93150	10.06850	9.88105		30
	40	9.81402	9.93406	10.06594	9.87996		20
	50	9.81549	9.93661	10.06339	9.87887		10
41°	00'	9.81694	9.93916	10.06084	9.87778	49°	00'
	10	9.81839	9.94171	10.05829	9.87668		50
	20	9.81983	9.94426	10.05574	9.87557		40
	30	9.82126	9.94681	10.05319	9.87446		30
	40	9.82269	9.94935	10.05065	9.87334		20
	50	9.82410	9.95190	10.04810	9.87221		10
42°	00'	9.82551	9.95444	10.04556	9.87107	48°	00'
	10	9.82691	9.95698	10.04302	9.86993		50
	20	9.82830	9.95952	10.04048	9.86879		40
	30	9.82968	9.96205	10.03795	9.86763		30
	40	9.83106	9.96459	10.03541	9.86647		20
	50	9.83242	9.96712	10.03288	9.86530		10
43°	00'	9.83378	9.96966	10.03034	9.86413	47°	00'
	10	9.83513	9.97219	10.02781	9.86295		50
	20	9.83648	9.97472	10.02528	9.86176		40
	30	9.83781	9.97725	10.02275	9.86056		30
	40	9.83914	9.97978	10.02022	9.85936		20
	50	9.84046	9.98231	10.01769	9.85815		10
44°	00'	9.84177	9.98484	10.01516	9.85693	46°	00'
	10	9.84308	9.98737	10.01263	9.85571		50
	20	9.84437	9.98989	10.01011	9.85448		40
	30	9.84566	9.99242	10.00758	9.85324		30
	40	9.84694	9.99495	10.00505	9.85200		20
	50	9.84822	9.99747	10.00253	9.85074		10
45°	00'	9.84949	10.00000	10.00000	9.84949	45°	00'
		Log Cos	Log Cot	Log Tan	Log Sin	Angle	

Index

Numbers refer to pages.

Abscissa, 16, 24
Absolute value, 151
Ambiguous case of general triangle, 134
Amplitude, 152
Angles
  Degree measure of, 4
  Of depression, 6
  Of elevation, 6
  Functions of complementary, 101
  Functions of half-, 92
  Initial side of, 23
  Measurement of, 3
  Negative, 104
  Positive, 23
  Radian measure of, 45
  Sexagesimal measure of, 4
  Terminal side of, 23
Arc, length of, 46
Area
  Of sector of circle, 48
  Of segment of circle, 49
  Of triangle, 68, 69
  (See *Summary*, 159.)
Axis
  Of coördinate system, 16, 24
  Of pure imaginary numbers, 150
  Of real numbers, 150

Base of system of logarithms, 114
Bearing of line, 8

Characteristic, 116
  Positive, 116
  Negative, 119
Complementary angles, functions of, 101
Complex numbers, 149
  Addition of, 152
  De Moivre's theorem, 154
  Graphical representation of, 150
  Modulus, 151
  Multiplication of, 153
  Powers of, 154

Roots of, 155
Subtraction of, 153
Trigonometric form of, 153
Components of vector, 51
Composition of vectors, 52
Circle
  Area of sector of, 48
  Area of segment of, 49
  Radius of circumscribed, 70
  Radius of inscribed, 70
Coördinates, 23, 24
Cosecant of angle, 24, 100
Cos $(A \pm B)$, 84, 88
Cos $A \pm \cos B$, 94
Cosine curve, 108
Cosine of angle, 24, 100
Cosine theorem, 62
Cotangent of angle, 24, 100

Degree measure of angle, 4
De Moivre's theorem, 154
Depression, angle of, 6

Elevation, angle of, 6
Equations
  Exponential, 123
  Solving trigonometric, 81
Exponential equations, 123

Functions
  Of $2A$, 90
  Of $\frac{1}{2}A$, 92
  Of 0°, 90°, and 180°, 89
  Of 30°, 45°, and 60°, 28
  Of 90° $\pm A$, 101
  Of 180° $\pm A$, 102
  Of acute angle, 25
  Of any angle, 15
  Of negative angles, 104
  Of obtuse angle, 57
  Reciprocal, 77
  Signs of, 100

Half-angles, functions of, 92
Horizontal line, 6

Identities, verifying, 78
Imaginary number, 149
Initial side of angle, 23
Inverse trigonometric functions, 109

Logarithm of number, 114
Logarithm tables, use of, 116, 121, 124-126

Mantissa, 116
Modulus, or absolute value, 151

Ordinate, 16, 24
Origin of coördinates, 16, 23

Plumb line, 6
Protractor, 4

Quadrant, 23

Radian, 45
Radian measure of angles, 45
Radius
  Of circumscribed circle, 70
  Of inscribed circle, 70
Reciprocal functions, 77
Resultant, 53

Scalar quantities, 50
Scale drawings, 2
Secant of angle, 24, 100
Sector of circle, area of, 48
Segment of circle, area of, 49
Sexagesimal measure of angle, 4
Similar triangles, 10
Sin $(A \pm B)$, 83, 86
Sin $A \pm \sin B$, 94
Sine curve, 106

Sine of angle, 19, 24, 100
Sine theorem, 59

Tangent $(A \pm B)$, 85, 88
Tangent curve, 109
Tangent half-angle theorem, 71
Tangent of angle, 15, 24, 100
Tangent theorem, 65
Terminal side of angle, 23
Theorem
  Cosine, 62
  De Moivre's, 154
  Sine, 59
  Tangent, 65
  Tangent half-angle, 71
Triangles
  Area of, 68
  Logarithms in solving, 129
  Ratios involving sides of, 15
  Of reference (scale), 26
  Similar, 10
  Solving the general, 57
  Solving right, 39
Triangulation, 145
Trigonometric equations, solving, 81
Trigonometric functions
  Graphs of, 106
  Inverse, 109
  Logarithms of, 124
  Of any angle defined, 22
  Use of table of, 31
  Variation of, 30

Vector, 50
  Components of, 51
  Composition of, 52
  Quantity, 50
Vertical line, 6